Yoga in Every Moment

DEAR BUFFIE,

    I WISH ✶ THAT THE NEW YEAR
WILL BRING FULFILLMENT OF ALL YOUR
IMPORTANT GOALS ... PEACE, LOVE, JOY, AND
ABUNDANCE FOR YOURSELF, YOUR FAMILY,
AND FRIENDS.
    WITH LOVE AND TENDERNESS,

        M₀

Yoga in Every Moment

Contemplations of a Yogi in the Midst of Life

Rama Berch

PUBLISHED BY
SVAROOPA TEACHING COLLECTIONS, INC.

Published by Svaroopa Teaching Collections, Inc.
450 Pearl Street, La Jolla, California 92037, USA
800.LUV.YOGA

SVAROOPA® is a registered service mark of S.T.C., Inc.

Printed in the United States of America.

ISBN: 1-930559-24-0

TABLE OF CONTENTS

PART III: INSIDE OUT

DEDICATION

CR

I dedicated my life long ago, and again every day, to my Guru, who is all that I have become and know I will be. It is from His blessings, training, love and support that I am able to dedicate this book to you – seekers of Truth, lovers of God and students of yoga everywhere.

Introduction

I was flying home from an extended stay in the *ashram* (residential yoga center) where I had been in training off and on for over fifteen years. My meditation kept deepening by the hour, in spite of the aircraft noise and cabin attendants' activity. Suddenly, a beautiful scene unfolded inside — a big white room with very high ceilings and lots of light shining through skylights and lots of windows. It had an ethereal quality to it. The ocean was just outside, though I could not see it. I felt instantly at home in the room. As soon as I had fully registered on the scene, the meditation abruptly ended. I did not know if I had seen heaven, if it were a dream, prediction of the future, or merely a concoction of my mind. But the feeling, as well as the look of it, was recorded somewhere deep inside me.

More than a year later, a real estate agent was showing me a possible new location for the growing Master Yoga Academy. As I walked into the main room, I recognized it. It was the same room, with the same feeling. The ocean was three blocks away. I knew that this was our new home. We moved in a few weeks later. It was the foundation for what is now six different facilities for classes, teacher training programs and our staff who serve the growing community of *Svaroopa Yogis*.

The story does not end there. About a year later, I was meeting with many of the *Svaroopa*-trained teachers in the local area. One of them turned to me and said, "You must be so happy to see all your dreams coming true." I laughed in astonishment, while tossing the pencil from my hands high into the air. "I would never have dreamed this big!" I thought again of the earlier vision, realizing that I was sitting in the reality that it became. And I knew — I would have limited myself so much, if it had been up to me. God has moved me far beyond where my puny mind would ever go.

Now I am offering you this collection of articles that I have been writing over the last ten years. My mind would have never allowed any of this to happen, if I had been following my mind. At this point, over 1,000 people have entered our Teacher Training programs, at least at the beginning level. I have originated and named a style of yoga that is nationally recognized and, as of this writing, is taught in eight countries. Additionally, I spend one-third of my year teaching at conferences and in yoga studios, supporting the teaching and practice of

Svaroopa Yoga internationally. I get to meet and touch a thousand people every year. It's a long way from a cave in the Himalayas!

It is quite synchronistic that I am writing this Introduction on Thanksgiving Day. I live in unspeakable gratitude to my teachers. Everything I do is an offering to them, as well as to you. My first yoga classroom was my living room. In 1976, I moved all the furniture out and painted the walls. I chanted to my teacher in India as I painted, knowing I was dedicating more than just the room. I was giving myself to yoga and to serving in every way. Each successive year of study and personal practice has dug my roots in a little deeper. This living yoga is like a loving fire that burns away the dross, leaving only the shine of pure gold behind. Yoga guarantees that your inner radiance will be progressively unveiled. It becomes a beacon that lights the world. It happens in stages. You can see some of my stages through these writings.

This collection is divided into three parts, based on when I wrote the articles as well as to whom they were addressed. You can watch my development as a teacher and writer over a full decade. Remember that yoga guarantees this progress, both on the inside as well as in your life. If I *did not* improve in the course of so many years of practice, there would be no reason for you to undertake the same process of Self-discovery.

In addition, what I wrote depended on the needs of the students. The topics I introduced, the examples I used, the conclusions I drew, and the practices I offered depended on those who were reading. You can see how the three sections mirror the readiness of the students who are traveling the path.

Part I: The Beginnings

These are the first articles I wrote, published in Master Yoga newsletters. My writing style reflects the way I was trained to teach, according to the traditional methods used in India. Yoga is described in broad and general terms. I explain both the theory and the practice. It is up to you to make it personal. How yoga works is explained, using everyday examples, to help you make it more immediate and tangible. The possibilities are clearly described, but you are the one who has to make them work.

The students receiving these articles were in the beginning of their yoga practice. These writings explain to them that there is a greater goal, in order to elicit their interest in yoga as a way of life. Yoga is much more than exercise.

At that time, the articles were intermittent publications. The chronology documents the developments, creating Master Yoga Foundation, our Statement of Purpose, and giving a name to our distinctive practice, *Svaroopa Yoga*. The process and goal of the *Svaroopa Yoga* practice is featured in a series of consecutive pieces written in the months after I named it.

Part II: Continuity

I began to find a more personal way of expressing the traditional teachings, drawing from my own life experiences. As yoga has been deepening the roots of my Being into Consciousness-Itself, I have been more able to let my own personality show. Just as every moment of my life becomes a living yoga, every experience becomes a possible teaching tool. This makes the articles progressively more personal over time. Students do not have to work so hard to integrate the yoga into their life, because the teaching is more personal and more real. It is not so much of a theory any more.

The very first article was titled <u>The Yoga of Relationship</u> (in Part I). My ability to be in this relationship has continued to develop, and the articles became more like a continuing conversation. It is like when you spend the weekend with friends or family. You start discussing something over dinner that first evening. The next morning, you pick up the same topic again. You return to it throughout the weekend while you are picnicking in the park, doing dishes together, watching a late movie, etc. You might continue the conversation next week in email, or next year when you get together again. But it is a continuing conversation within the context of a continuing relationship. In this section, I am speaking to students who are deepening in their practice and understanding their life in a new way.

The frequency of the newsletters became more regular. The chronological arrangement in this collection allows you to track the monthly flow through the seasons over succeeding years. Certain themes recur: gratitude — every autumn, holidays — each December. Each January speaks of new beginnings and offers a reminder of the importance of making resolutions.

Simultaneously, a thread of continuity develops — the underlying theme of finding and living from your true Self. Themes developed into monthly articles, which became the basis for contemplations. I began sending a selection of quotes for our teachers to share with their students in class. These contemplations give students something to chew on, to digest the yoga teachings in bite size pieces. A few are included here with each article.

You may find one that you want to copy down — put it on your refrigerator, bathroom mirror or the dashboard on your car. When you construct these daily reminders for yourself, you continue the yoga of working on your mind. In addition, we excerpted some quotes from the articles and published them in a daily contemplations journal, _Seeds of the Soul_. It is the daily things that make the biggest difference.

Part III: Inside Out

These articles spoke to a different audience, the general public. Published in various magazines and publications, the collection developed simultaneously with the newsletter articles in the first two sections. Rather than being arranged chronologically, these are in a thematic flow.

Since these readers were not practicing yogis, the beginning pieces introduced yoga as a comprehensive science. The challenges of life were addressed in a broad way that led into the foundational principles of yoga philosophy. At the same time that the pieces are more broad, they also offer more details. Examples include the articles about _karma_ and reincarnation. I included these specifics in order to help dispel widespread misconceptions. More importantly, in this venue, there is no opportunity for continuing conversation. The readers may never read another article. They are not coming to class and cannot ask their personal questions, so they need more information to carry away with them.

While this information can be helpful, it actually brings us full circle back to the teaching of the _theory_ of yoga. Without the personal experiences that yoga practice provides, theory can actually impede your progress. You are capable of using the theory to become better at beating yourself up. If you add up all of the theory, it does not measure up to even one hour of practice. Remember, you must do it and you must live in it in order to "get it."

There is no real ending to this book. The expanding awareness and deepening sense of Self does not end. It just gets better and better. I am still deepening into yoga, myself. I hope to be able to continue to serve you in your developing ability to know your Self. Yoga keeps expanding your capacity until the words "you" and "me" have no meaning any more. Most importantly, we are still doing yoga.

Namaste.

November 22, 2001

PART I

❧

Initiation

The Yoga of Relationship

May 1992

I have written the Statement of Purpose for our new Master Yoga Foundation with "Cultivating our innate yearning for transcendence." This yearning for "something more" in life is what impels you to action. You try to satisfy this innate longing by achieving or by buying great things, or by having significant relationships. To accomplish great things, to own beautiful possessions and to have good relationships is healthy, but is that really enough?

The problem with looking to your relationships to satisfy this inner longing is that you put pressure on the other person. This is defined as dysfunctional, meaning that it does not work. It cannot work, because that for which you truly yearn can be found only inside your own being. The moments you connect with it while you are with another person are profound, but it is the connection with your own inner essence that gives these relational experiences their significance. Trying to find that feeling again by recreating the externals (eating at the same restaurant, listening to the same album, or having a similar conversation) will guarantee inconsistent results.

The intimate connection that you seek with another person is more than a meeting of minds and more than a meeting of bodies. The point at which communication becomes communion is the experience of union. This is the goal of yoga, and the meaning of the Sanskrit word "yoga" itself — union. Once your innate yearning connects with your own inner source that fills it, you experience this connection and communion with everyone. It is the natural outward expression of the inner experience.

My own experience of relationships has been transformed by yoga. I have difficulty naming it "love." It is somehow both more and less than what I always thought love was. Whatever you want to call it, it is yoga. This is what makes our relationships work. For me, it includes a deep respect for every person, along with a genuine interest and caring for how they think, how they feel, and for what is going on in their lives.

Because of this, I never tire of talking with students about their lives, about their body, about their feelings, and especially about their experiences of yoga. I feel deeply honored by their sharing with me. I am grateful for this opportunity to share my understanding and my experience of yoga with you, through these articles. I look forward to continuing my learning and the process of transcendence through this relationship with you.

Discipline
September 1992

In yoga, discipline is not the same as "spare the rod and spoil the child" — punishment and enforcement. Yogic discipline is the means by which you are uplifted and transformed. It is how you can get the highest and the best from your yoga practice. Continued application of your own effort, on a regular basis, is what makes you successful at anything in your life: yoga, art, business, relationships, etc.

The best athletes and musicians must practice daily, yet they do not consider it an onerous duty. Top musicians love to do the scales! True discipline is doing regularly what makes you feel best. Regularity is the key, and it is what ultimately makes it easy. Consider who creates this regularity? Your job may require you to keep certain hours. This then determines when you eat, get up, go to bed, and have free time. A newly self-employed or retired person often has difficulty organizing these things, because they are used to an externally imposed discipline. Yet, even enforced discipline can yield great benefits. A woman in her '60's told me she hated her mother for sending her to piano lessons and making her practice every day. Now the piano is one of the greatest joys in her life. In yoga class you experience the benefits of externally imposed discipline when you do *Uttana Padasana* (Leg Circles), which I often describe (tongue-in-cheek) as "everybody's favorite pose."

External discipline can be imposed by force, or it can be by our own choice, like belonging to a sports team or having a very demanding job. You have the interest and you choose to participate, but others still get you moving. The team practices are set up by the coach or your boss assigns your responsibilities. This is one of the main reasons yoga is offered in classes. The day and time you come to class creates regularity for you, as an externally generated discipline. You choose to participate and you get yourself there which is sometimes the hardest part. Then the teacher gets you into poses you might not do at home. In addition to learning more about yoga, you are actually *doing it*. This is the secret to discipline, and the secret to getting benefit from anything. Just do it.

This is what internally generated discipline is — Just do it! You already do this with many things in your life. Why do you bathe or shower daily? No one checks on you. No one sets the time for you. You could skip a day or just do a light sponge bath. No one would even know. But you bathe. Why? This is discipline, also called habit. Internally generated discipline, or self-discipline, is the same as habit. It is not "forcing yourself" to do the things you know you should do. It is doing these things because they are a part of your life.

How did you develop these self-disciplines, these habits? This is the important part. *You learned them.* You were taught to bathe daily. You may have objected to it at some point in your childhood, but you internalized it. Now you even enjoy it. Everything you do, you learned. The things you do regularly actually determine the quality of your life.

You can learn (or unlearn) anything, if you choose to. You already know how you feel after doing some yoga. So how often do you do it? I frequently get phone calls where the caller says, "I never felt better in my life than when I was in yoga classes *two years ago*. I need to get back."

Perhaps the real question is, "How good are you willing to feel on a daily basis?" To establish a daily habit, you need only to do some yoga every day. It takes just a little effort. Yoga always stresses the importance of discipline and regularity. Participation in any yoga class, regularly or irregularly, is good. The results are obvious by the end of class, and they last for hours or days. But these results increase over time when you come on the same day each week. Your body and mind both love that kind of regularity. Your body and mind get accustomed to their regular Monday night (or whenever) — opening-up, tuning-up, and deep relaxation in yoga class.

This also explains why our classes are structured on a thematic basis. When you work through the theme for the whole month, you get even more results. After a month of abdominals, one student confided, "I have been constipated for thirty-seven years, and now I am not." While working on the month of standing poses, another student shares, "Now I'm noticing how I stand at work. It makes a real difference." Our theme handouts describe the specific goals and benefits for each theme. You can recognize the benefits as you are getting them, and seeing the results motivates you to keep going.

When you cannot attend your regular class, you can always go to another. It is better to come to any class than to miss it completely. But regular practice means both coming to class on regular days and times, as well as doing some yoga on your own. Then see for yourself how much you get out of it!

Formless & Form

December 1992

The Formless pervades and animates your form. Form is meaningless without the Formless. It enlivens you; it makes you alive. It even makes you able to enjoy being alive. When you are not enjoying being alive, you actually become less alive. In yoga, the answer to everything is to become more alive. Then, the things that seem to be the cause of unhappiness become less significant. They are more like pebbles along the path rather than boulders or cliffs. You can achieve this through the yoga practices: *asana* (poses), *pranayama* (breathing), *pratyahara* (turning inward), *dharana* (contemplation), and *dhyana* (meditation).

Each year you celebrate your birthday. To honor the anniversary of your birth is to say that you are glad to be alive. Are you glad you are alive? More than this, who is it that is being glad of this? Even more importantly, who is it that is alive? I recently considered these questions myself. I felt an inner presence arise strongly within me, saying so beautifully, "I AM HERE!" In that inner surge I felt the power of my own presence. I felt the real "I" that I am. I could feel this "I" which enlivens any form. This is the Formless, within form.

The Formless pervades and animates your form, your physical body. Without it, your body is dead. A lifeless body is not attractive to anyone. A student recently shared how she felt when she saw the lifeless form of her mother. She saw so clearly that the person she had known and loved was not present any more. She found it easy to give up her attachment to her mother's form, because it was meaningless without the Formless being present in it.

Moisture pervades air. Humidity is a measure of the moisture content of the air. The Formless pervades your form, but it is different than the moisture in air. The water content in the air is different and separate from the air. The Formless in your form is not different and separate from your body. The Formless produces your body without being limited by it. Think of it as the energy which becomes the atoms that create your physical body. The Formless within you creates or generates the energy that becomes your form. It can also be called "spirit." It makes you feel spirited or inspired. To live fully infused with this Reality is the goal of all spiritual paths. We begin every yoga class with *Shavasana* in order to focus on being fully present, so you can experience your own aliveness in its pure form/formlessness.

Asanas (poses) are a way of weaving the form and Formless together. These don't actually need to be interwoven because the Formless creates and animates your form. But your awareness of this is currently limited. This is the same as being inert, like a rock. Your body becomes stiff and hard, like a rock. It doesn't move and bend. It is not fluid like water, but becomes dense like rock. It is less alive — and so are you. This is why yoga gets you moving and bending and breathing. All the while, you turn your attention to the feeling of the moving, bending and breathing. You first extend your awareness into your form. Then you can go to the next step: you become aware of awareness itself. What is this awareness? What is this aliveness?

Yoga includes the moving, bending and breathing as a means to discover the answers to these questions and others, as well. What is the light that shines in your eyes? This is the Formless. It is this which yoga worships. The teachings of yoga begin with, "You are perfect and divine. Know this Truth, and live it." When you hear it as a beautiful teaching, it is only a theory. Living yoga means to move beyond theory and into the experience of being fully alive. Do more yoga.

The Changeless Principle

June 1993

"The one thing constant in life is change," advises an ancient Greek philosopher. Yoga goes one step further. In the midst of change, there is an inner principle that remains steady. The constancy of your own presence never leaves you. However, you may not be looking inward to find it. If you define yourself by the outer situations, your sense of self changes with the changes of life. One moment you will be happy, and the next moment you will not. If you measure your self by your net worth, or if you are merely at the mercy of the evening news, you'll be living on a roller coaster, rising and falling from heaven to an inner hell.

People react differently to change. Some people live for change. Others like to have a choice in the change. Some people resist change; others are relieved when it is thrust upon them. The most adaptable and flexible people are those with an inner sense core of stability. They handle and enjoy whatever life offers. One Sanskrit text describes this by stating, "Realizing the inner Truth, one can live anywhere."

Certain yoga practices develop this inner sense of stability, while engendering flexibility. You must have both stability and flexibility. Then, you can live anywhere and enjoy every moment of life, not in spite of what it brings, but because of what it brings. With this inner steadiness, you can be flexible without being a doormat. You will not need to use your old tactics: to resist, to hide from or to control change. You will not have to create change in order to avoid having it thrust upon you. All these tactics have one major drawback, primarily loss of joy. Life is meant to be a joyful experience, with your welcoming each moment of each day, even when the unexpected occurs. You will not experience this joy if you are always controlling the external components to try to make your life seem perfect.

Your inner Self is the one changeless principle. When life is swirling around outside of you, your inner Self remains serene and undisturbed. This serene center is called "Self" or "That." You are That. You have always been and will always be That. You can never lose That. When you know That, it supports you through the fluctuations inherent in life.

A Sanskrit verse describes this as *niralambaya*, needing no support. You do not depend on an outer role or identity to prop up your sense of self. Your actions and words come from the changeless inner principle. The goal of yoga is for you to live in this state. It is already familiar to you, because you get a taste of it at the end of every class. This inner assurance eliminates any need to defend or protect yourself. It is never affected by stress or hurry. It is the deep experience of your inner Self in every moment.

Once you've found it, it fills into the other parts of your life. This inner support becomes tangible in every moment of your day. When this is not your day, you turn to crutches for support of your sense of self. Let go of these crutches, because any crutch will ultimately be lost. A personal crisis arises because your crutches are threatened or lost. Is your car or your extensive wardrobe irreplaceable? I know someone whose home burned down and she lost everything. If this happened to you, would you still exist?

Of course, you would still exist. And you would have an excellent opportunity to look beyond external crutches and find the changeless principle within. The real meaning of life comes from your inner Self. This is what yoga gives you. You taste it in *Shavasana* (Relaxation Pose). It is there in every yoga pose. You can perfect it in meditation. In this way your practice of yoga becomes the perfect preparation for life — you are able to find the changeless principle even in the midst of life's changes. Then, every change is a celebration of life itself! Do more yoga!

How Does It Work?

October 1993

Yoga gives you more than exercise does. While you get all of the benefits of any other type of exercise program, yoga also:

- relieves stress
- provides mental clarity
- grants inner peace and serenity
- promotes healing on all levels
- creates personal transformation
- bestows the natural bliss of being alive
- explains the goal and purpose of life, and helps you get it.

It always does all of these things. That is quite incredible. Yoga strengthens your body, makes you more flexible and gives you all of these additional benefits *every time you do it*. It's called instant gratification. Plus, the effects are cumulative. Each time you do yoga, your starting point has progressed. You have the benefits from all the previous classes or sessions already there, so the effects of your new session are even more obvious and enjoyable. How does it work?

If you turn on your kitchen faucet, the water flows out on its own. You do not have to pump the water out. When you get in a pose, yoga flows through you—as if the water has been turned on. Yoga classes work from this basic principle. This water-like flow is the "juice of life." When it flows through your body, you experience bliss. When it flows through your mind, you have unparalleled mental clarity. When it flows through your heart, you experience all-encompassing love. But tensions on any level restrict the flow.

The purpose of yoga is to turn on the tap again. It works on all the levels of your existence, all at the same time. This is very easy to recognize. Tension in your mind creates tension in your body. It blocks your ability to relax. If you have ever lain awake at night, you know how your mind can keep you from getting needed rest. When life changes and that worry is gone, your great sigh of relief is more than a deep breath. It lets your whole mind and body relax. You feel younger and lighter. Yoga uses this relationship by turning it around: Your body is used to release mental tensions. Some of those deep seated tensions have become so familiar that you no longer notice them. Now you notice because they are gone!

The collected tensions are actually the physical expression of mental and emotional constrictions. They lodge in your body. You may notice them settle in your shoulders, low back or anywhere else. They may constrict your breathing, impair your digestion or give other discomfort. They leave you in a state of fatigue and depression. But they are not a never-ending curse over which you have no control. The practice of yoga gives you choice about how you feel.

The difficulty is that many of the poses are hard, if you are more than two years old. Back then, you could still chew on your toes and turn somersaults with ease. Your energy level was limitless; you exhausted the adults around you. Where did it all go? You can get your body moving again. Regular yoga practice does this gradually and compassionately. It takes time to develop your ability to do some of the poses, but you are getting all the benefits all along the way.

The amount you get is in direct proportion to the amount you do. If you want to get more from yoga, it does not mean you have to "work harder." Yes, you will sweat in yoga class sometimes, but more sweat is not the goal. More bliss is the goal. What you need to do is to get rid of the tensions in your body, mind, heart and the deeper levels of your being. You do not have to force your body to do a pose; you finesse the pose so your body can reclaim its original flexibility.

The poses that are initially hard become surprisingly easy when you don't have to work through tensions that prevent full range of movement. Does a two-year-old child have to work hard to reach his or her toes? Not only does that two-year-old have a more open body, but also a more open mind and heart. Their souls shine through their eyes so clearly that you easily fall in love with them.

The key is to stay in the pose by aligning yourself so that it is easy. Then you can stay long enough for the yoga to flow. You do not have to compel the changes. You can concentrate on the physical level, and you will get all that yoga offers. Our classes aim at the full yoga experience. So, how does it work? If you want more out of life, you will find it inside.

The Power of Yoga

January 1994

The pace of our modern lifestyle challenges everyone. It is called stress. In the *Bhagavadgita*, Krishna speaks to his student and friend Arjuna. He says what we call stress is due to attachment, and that you must abandon attachment. What is attachment?

Attachment is dependence on certain results in order to feel good. You may or may not be good at getting the results you want. The *Bhagavadgita* says that your effectiveness is not the point. You will experience pain and suffering whether you're successful or not, as long as your motive is the getting of the results.

For example, at work you want to complete a certain project. You work long hours at it and try to make it perfect. When it is complete you feel great. You are congratulated by your peers. You may earn a promotion or raise. But now you have a back or neck problem or your spouse is unhappy about never seeing you. Pain and suffering will always result from being attached to your actions.

Instead, you may be overwhelmed by the size of the project. So, you never begin. The boss sees that nothing is being done and gives it to someone else to do. Now you are resentful or even want revenge. Pain and suffering result from being attached to inaction.

The first is attachment to action; the second is attachment to inaction. Attachment to action creates an endless cycle of relentless activity, physical and mental. Your mind can exhaust you. Attachment to inaction is dark and heavy. The inertia can paralyze you. Thus, it seems you can neither act nor refrain from action. What can you do?

This is the subject of the *Bhagavadgita*. It is an extraordinary primer on how to live your life. It describes the human condition and how to lift yourself up out of it. It describes the transcendent state of an exalted human being, as well as how to become one. Krishna is speaking to Arjuna on the battlefield, and tells him to do his duty.

"Perform actions, having abandoned attachment." To act without attachment is incredibly liberating. You have done this, probably many times before. To help an elderly person with their grocery bags, or to take home a lost dog and phone the owner is an act of service. When you do these things without expectation of reward, you feel great. There's no pain or suffering because there was no attachment. Krishna says, "Your right is to action alone; never to its fruits at any time." As a yogi, you learn to perform all your actions in this way, "having become indifferent to success or failure." You can do your work very well, for the pure pleasure of it, regardless of whether others will commend you or not. In this way you have a life that is truly divine.

Krishna further says, "Evenness of mind is yoga." This is not the same as always feeling bland or flat. That is a type of inaction that can deaden your ability to enjoy life. True evenness of mind comes about from being "fixed in yoga." You can finally step off the emotional roller coaster, to become steady in your own center. The word yoga means union, referring to the constant connection with your inner source of inspiration, love and joy. When you are steady in this inner experience, you perform your actions in total freedom. Your life is full, because you are being constantly filled from the inside out.

What Kind of Yoga?
April 1994

I am often asked, "What kind of yoga do you teach?" How can we describe an experience of the wordless place of perfect being that is inherent in every person? Is it possible to describe the way we use the body and the breath to help open the doorway inside? The bodily sensations and physical changes we work with are virtually incomprehensible to the caller on the phone. It is only in class that the newcomer can experience some of what we are pointing out.

Yoga's resurgence of popularity has created a well-educated public who has heard of different "types" of yoga. These name brands are simply different styles of the generic *hatha yoga*, though the new yogi may not know that. Each style is a different approach to the same poses, and is a reflection of the personality of the founder. It's similar to spaghetti. If we each make a pot of spaghetti, they will be quite different. Yet, they're all spaghetti. When you are shopping, name brands are useful, offering a reliable flavor each time you buy a certain brand of spaghetti sauce.

The need to describe our style of *hatha yoga* has been intensifying over the years. Thus, I have been contemplating for some time what name should specify our style. I enlisted the help of several key advisors, members of our Board of Directors and experts in yoga philosophy. Through research, contemplation, meditation, and prayer, one name has arisen: *Svaroopa Yoga*.

To understand its meaning, begin with the word "yoga". It comes from the Sanskrit root *yuj*, which means to unite or to yoke together. Thus, yoga means connection or union of the mundane with the spiritual, of the self with the Self, or of the individual (you) with the divine. However, the *Pratyabhijnahrdayam* makes it clear that yoga is not a connection, but a reconnection. The word "yoga" does not mean union of two separate things, but the reunion of those things which only seemed to be separate. The text states:

*Chitivahnir avarohapade channo'pi
maatrayaa meyendhanam plushyati.*

Chiti does not lose Her nature even when She
becomes the individual, but like fire burns
the fuel of objective knowledge.
- *Pratyabhijnahrdayam* #14

13

This means that, while you experience yourself as being separate from everything, you have a deeper sense of your true Self behind the scenes. Just behind the thoughts and activity of your mind, there is a deeper knowing which is an inner certitude of Being that you rarely access. This is *Chiti*, which is Consciousness-Itself. This is who you really are. As an individual, you identify with specifics that define you, as being limited by the circumstances of your birth as well as and what you have done since then. Yet, your true Self is not limited. The word "yoga" means the reunion of your seemingly limited self with your true Self, *Chiti*. This deeper knowledge is always burning inside, propelling you onto the path of rediscovery.

The word "yoga" is often used to refer to the practices, including poses, breathing, meditation, chanting, focusing techniques, and more. These practices give you access to the inner experience of true Self. Along the way you also become stronger, more flexible, healthier, happier, and more positive about life. Thus, many people are drawn to *yoga* for these obvious benefits. Some name brands of yoga even characterize these practices and their physical benefits as the goal of yoga. But yoga does not mean exercise, or even meditation. Yoga means the inner experience of union that is your birthright as a human being.

I am very fortunate to have been introduced to yoga by a Master who showed me the true meaning of the word "Yoga" at once. I have since understood how the practices are used both to find the inner experience and to live in this inner certitude of Being. So, everything we offer at Master Yoga is designed to take you home again, to the inner reunion that is the only thing that really matters.

Now consider the word s*varoopa*, a compound of *sva-* and *roopa*. *Sva* means Self— the Truth or Reality of your being. *Roopa* means form or shape, and refers to your physical body. This is particularly relevant in *hatha yoga*, because you are working with your body in the poses, breathing and guided relaxations. Modern physicists have described how our physical world is actually comprised of swirls of energy moving at incredible speeds through vast amounts of empty space. Your own body is part of the physical world, made of the same energy, moving through empty space.

In *Svaroopa Yoga*, we use the physical body (*roopa*) as the gateway to perceive this other level of Reality (*sva*), the energy which is manifesting as your own body. This energy ("*Chiti*") manifests as the world, emanating from the Source which is ever full, whole and perfect. All the omni's apply: omniscient, omnipresent, omnipotent, and eternal. All of them apply to you. *Chiti*, manifesting as you, never loses that divine nature, never becomes something less. Consciousness only seems to take on the limitations and the sense of separateness that characterize your human experience. By delving into and through your own body, you come to know your true Self, which is the Source of all Existence.

In the *Yoga Sutras*, *Patanjali* uses the word *svaroopa* to describe the purpose of yoga practice. First, he explains that yoga is the stilling of the activity of your mind. Why? Because as soon as your mind stops, your essential nature *(svaroopa)* bursts forth in all its glory. It was always there behind the scenes, but you were distracted by the activity of your mind.

The name *Svaroopa Yoga* describes both our goal in yoga, and the means we use to attain it. We use your physical form *(roopa)* to access your true form *(svaroopa)*. We are practicing yoga for its original purpose, described by the sages thousands of years ago.

Now, when someone asks you what kind of yoga you practice, you can answer: *Svaroopa Yoga*. But, keep in mind that *Svaroopa Yoga* could be considered a redundancy, for both words mean the same thing: reunion with your own true nature.

Tadaa drashtuh svaroope 'vasthaanam.

Then the Seer is established in his own essential and fundamental nature (*svaroopa*).
- *Patanjali's Yoga Sutras* 1.3

Svaroopa Yoga #1
June 1994

Our style of hatha yoga is named *Svaroopa Yoga* because we use the poses to discover *svaroopa* inside. This experience *of svaroopa*, your own true form, is the goal of yoga practice. Your true form is consciousness, beyond all limitations of idea, understanding or individuality. The experience of *svaroopa* is very easy to access, and is found within and beyond the layers of individuality where you normally get stuck. It can be described as bliss, but the <u>Shiva Sutras</u> describe it as an aliveness that cannot be imagined — only experienced.

Chaitanyam atma

**The Self is consciousness,
completely enlivened, fully aware.**

- Shiva Sutras 1.1

Atma is your true Self, the essence of your being. It can be considered a synonym for *svaroopa*, your true form. *Svaroopa* points to the experience of *Atma*, while *Atma* highlights that there is something to experience.

In this text, Shiva starts his message by telling us the most important thing in the first *Sutra*: You are Consciousness. This is completely different than how we usually describe ourselves. We tell others, "I am tall" or "I am a teacher," or "I am angry." We tell ourselves, "I am not good enough," "I am overworked and underappreciated," or "I am too fat." We rarely tell ourselves anything positive, but even a positive statement would be limited. Even affirmations are limited, and limiting. The most powerful affirmation you can use is, "I am consciousness." Most mantras given by great Masters actually mean this.

This consciousness (that is who you are) is completely alive. To feel completely alive is an extraordinary thing. You have had this experience at some time in your life. I vividly remember the moment I began to walk down the church aisle when I got married. I was fully alive. I could see everything and everyone there. I was absolutely still inside, completely calm. And I radiated a glow that was more than happiness — it felt holy.

At the time, it seemed that the experience was due to the external conditions: it was my wedding day. Since then, I have had that experience many times. The sages tell us we can have this experience at any time, by simply choosing to be in it. Who would ever choose to be out of it, once you had the ability choose it?

This is *Svaroopa Yoga*, a way to use yoga poses and breathing to find this experience inside. You do not have to wait for the *Shavasana* relaxation pose at the end of a yoga class, but you can find it in every pose. More than that, you can find it in every beam of light, in every leaf on every tree, in every breath you breathe, and in every moment of life. Even now. Just consider: Who are you, really?

Svaroopa Yoga #2

July 1994

Your body is a gateway to consciousness. By working with your body, you can open your awareness to the subtler levels of consciousness that are your true form, *svaroopa*. This is the goal of yoga: your own inner experience of your own being as Consciousness-Itself.

Tadaa drashtuh svaroope 'vasthaanam

Then you are established in your own essential and fundamental nature.

- Patanjali Yoga Sutras 1.3

You are alive, but your aliveness is something different than the aliveness of an insect, a bird or even a dog. This quality that is unique to human beings is called consciousness, and it can be experienced directly. Your own inner experience of it is called *svaroopa*, your true form. It is always there, even though you may not be experiencing that bliss of your own being all the time.

There are many ways to turn inward and access that inner level. Different practices of yoga work with your body, your mind or your heart as a way inside. Working with your body through *Svaroopa Yoga* is one of the easiest ways to gain direct access to *svaroopa*. That profound inner experience is deeply healing. It will heal your body. It will also heal all the hurts stored in your heart and memory, while it frees you from the repetitive tendencies of your mind.

However, there is a hazard in the practice *Svaroopa Yoga*. You can get caught up in trying to perfect your body. You can obsess on making your body match some internalized image of how it "should be" that bears no relationship to reality. Actually, these internalized images are often the cause of problems, even in other areas of your life, especially in relationships.

When you are doing a pose, if you are trying to place your body in the "perfect" pose, see what guideline are you using for that image of "perfection." You have probably internalized an image based on a photo, a video, or someone else's demonstration of the pose. Is that what your body needs? It is possible that your body is not supposed to be like their body. Do not let that image become your goal!

Svaroopa Yoga is a way of working with what your body really needs, instead of with how you wish it were. It brings you right back to reality, starting with your physical form. Your experience of that outer level of reality will link you to the deeper inner level of Reality, *svaroopa*. We teach you to find that deeper reality by beginning with your body.

The physical aspect of every pose has an external component and an internal component. You can see the external physical component, which is how the pose looks. It is the least important. You cannot see the internal physical component, like your tailbone. You must feel it. The areas in your body that you cannot feel correlate to the areas of consciousness you cannot access. When you use the poses to create gentle and reliable opening through the deep levels of musculature (which you cannot see), you open the gateway to the inner levels of your own consciousness. Then, as *Patanjali* says, you will experience *svaroopa*. It is so easy. Do more yoga.

Svaroopa Yoga #3

August 1994

Your body is made of the same "stuff" of which everything in the world is made. The basic component of all existence is energy, clearly described by modern physics. The small energy-bits move at incredibly fast speeds on a background of space, which physicists used to call "empty space." Now they tell us that it is not empty. They have also discovered that the swirling energy is conscious. Every bit of energy is conscious, and is in constant communication with every other bit of energy. How wonderful!

Your body is made of this energy, tiny bits of contracted energy masquerading as subatomic particles. These combine into atoms, becoming molecules, cells, bones, skin, hair, eyes, etc. Even your mind and thoughts are a subtle manifestation of this energy. The ancient sages knew this. They used their own bodies and minds as a spectrophotometer through which to view energy at its primary level. They told us, "What is within is outside." They exhorted us to explore ourselves in order to know everything and everyone. This is still true today.

Yoga is the rediscovery of this knowing of both inside and outside. Of the many types of yoga, *hatha yoga* is a way of working with your body to prepare for the ecstatic experience of this inner knowing. *Svaroopa Yoga* is a way to work with your body to create immediate experiences of this vast knowing of your own being, to improve your ability to deepen this ecstatic experience, and to stay in it for longer and longer periods.

In teaching *Svaroopa Yoga*, we recognize multiple levels of reality in your own body as we work with it. Your body is tangible: bones, muscles, internal organs, etc. Your body is also intangible — conscious energy swirling in a vast field of non-empty space. This is the wonder of being alive. Every human being has the incredible capacity to know both realities simultaneously. You can live in both realities. You do not have to choose between one or the other.

All pain and unhappiness comes from your not knowing. "Limited knowledge is bondage," says the *Jnanam bandhah (Shiva Sutras* 1.2). Our condition is one of bondage or limitation. We take the tangible world as reality and limit our knowing to what we see on the outside. Without the deeper level of knowing, we wither on the vine like a fruit that is not getting nourishment from the roots of the plant. We must tap into the root of our being to be nourished, "True Knowing is the only food that really nourishes" (*Jnaanam annam, Shiva Sutras* 2.9).

We try so many different ways to tap into that source of nourishment. We go on vacation, read books, watch the sunset, indulge in chocolate (or try drugs or alcohol), have sex, go to the Comedy Club, buy our (current) heart's desire, exercise, sing, pray, dance, laugh, cry, etc. All of these are actually forms of seeking. You are a "seeker." Sometimes these things work; sometimes they do not. Some of them are good for us; some of them are not.

Yoga gives a way to connect to that foundational level of your own Being, and then stay there. All forms of outer seeking are actually the inner yearning to know this aspect of your own nature, the source of your own existence. If this is the "stuff" from which you are made, there must be a way to know it.

Svaroopa Yoga uses your body as a gateway to the inner experience of consciousness. It works because your body is made of that consciousness. However, to explore that conscious energy of your own body requires a certain attitude, a specific type of approach. A superficial approach will give you superficial results — you *can* perfect your body. Yoga poses can be used to make you strong and healthy, and to keep you young, fit and beautiful. This attitude or approach *will* work. You will get what you seek, though becoming strong, young, and beautiful does not guarantee you happiness.

If you can do yoga poses with the intention of knowing the truth of your own consciousness, you will get that. You will also become strong and healthy. You will be young, fit and beautiful. And you will be deeply and profoundly happy, because the experience of pure consciousness makes you very happy. Your experience is beyond "happy," for that word is too limiting. The sages say you will experience bliss or ecstasy. Your inner experience of *Svaroopa*, the Bliss of your own Being, will overflow into your life, and into the lives of all around you.

The yoga poses must be approached in a certain way to create this bridge between the outer and inner levels. Instead of posing or performing, you are exploring. Instead of fixing your body, you are finessing it. Instead of exercising, you are opening your body and Being. Instead of wrestling with your body as though it were a mechanical object, you are making it more alive and more conscious. Instead of relaxing into oblivion, you are becoming more aware — until you discover you are awareness yourself. Do more yoga.

Svaroopa Yoga #4
September 1994

Do you have any problem spots in your body? Have you any familiar aches and pains that flare up intermittently, or that you carry with you all the time? These are actually the tip of the iceberg. Unfortunately, if you continue to ignore them, they continue to evolve. The end result hopefully will not be chronic pain or partial/complete disability, but may simply be called aging. It is uncomfortable — and completely unnecessary.

One yoga student frequently describes her stiff neck to me. She is continually reminded of it because she cannot turn her head when she drives. More than this, she can barely reach her feet to tie her shoes, standing or seated. Her neck problem will not actually improve until her whole body improves. Her neck is the tip of the iceberg. The rest of the iceberg (the stiffness in her whole body) is submerged beneath the surface of her awareness. She is completely oblivious to the need for her whole body to improve. She just wants her neck to be better. Fortunately, she continues to attend regular yoga classes and her whole body is improving. So her neck will improve, too.

A problem spot in your body is an indicator that your whole body needs attention. It may even motivate you to get to your first yoga class. Then you will discover the rest of the iceberg, the frozen (non-moving) areas of your body that you had blocked from your awareness.

It is good to get your body moving again. It is important to be free from pain. It feels wonderful to have your body becoming younger and more alive. Yoga offers you all this. Yet yoga considers these things to be side-benefits, like the ocean views you see on the drive north to Orange County. Few people make the drive north just to see the views. Most of us merely enjoy them on the way to the destination.

The destination or goal of yoga is the experience of your own true form, *svaroopa*. This is the inner knowing of the essence of your own existence. It is the Conscious Source from which you originate and into which you will merge again. The goal of yoga is the ecstatic knowing of your own consciousness. The ways in which your body is frozen are ways that your experience of your own true form is blocked. When you get your body moving again, you reopen these gateways inside.

Your body is made of energy. Modern physicists describe the conscious energy that makes up all of existence including the energy template which becomes your body. You can work with your body to change your mind, and you can use your mind to change your body, but it is ultimately the template that must be changed. Yoga poses and breathing start the process of making these changes. The most effective way to make changes in the template is through meditation. In deep meditation, you dip into the pure consciousness that is your own Self. Each time you merge into this Inner Reality, your template changes at the most rapid rate possible.

In *Svaroopa Yoga*, we work with all these levels simultaneously. Do more yoga!

The Yoga Of Self-Inquiry
November 1994

Do you ever hear yourself saying, "What did I do wrong?" "Why is this happening to me?" "Here we go, again." "When am I *ever* going to get the lesson?" This is a form of self-inquiry, but not yogic self-inquiry.

Yoga describes your "edges," the ways in which you are not aware of your true nature, as divine and perfect consciousness. There are places in your life where you experience that fullness of your own being, and places where you do not. You draw back from certain things, have attachments to others, and resist or deny others. You even go around in circles, repeating the same patterns throughout your life. Many would call this "human nature."

Yoga redefines human nature as divine, perfect consciousness. To know that inner Self means you will melt all your edges, like an ice cube melting into the ocean of consciousness. The yoga practice of self-inquiry *(svadhyaya)* makes you able to inquire into your true human nature — your divine nature.

Everyone is doing self-inquiry, badly. Everyone is talking to everyone else about all their problems and all the things they do not like. Television is full of it. So are the movies, our music and magazines. If you did not focus on those things, what would you have to talk about?

In class, the yoga poses evoke the experience of your own true nature, *svaroopa*. This is why we call it *Svaroopa Yoga*. We use your body to give you access to that level of your own being, as your first step in *svadhyaya* (self-inquiry). This avoids the pitfalls of your usual mode of circular analysis and self-judgement. The body never analyzes or judges. It only experiences.

First, you learn to use your body as the point of focus. You are really learning how to use the beam of consciousness that streams through your mind in a new way. That light of consciousness is like the rays of the sun, but you've been using it as if you were a firefly. Directing this beam of your awareness to (and through) your body has a salutory effect on your body. More importantly, it gives you the tools to go to deeper inner levels, in order to look at your mind, your heart and your life.

We offer contemplations at the end of every class as further training in *svadhyaya*. They give you a way to deepen your understanding of yoga and of your life. They also help you take yoga into your world in a very tangible way, so your yoga practice begins to fill your whole life, and overflow to change the world.

24

Receiving the Gift
December 1994

I was an achiever. From my childhood, I understood that performing well offers its own rewards. I tackled many tasks in life, mastered many skills, and tired of them just as quickly. Nothing held my interest, but my ability to propel myself forward was reliable. Ultimately, I propelled myself right into yoga.

Fortunately, my habitual style paid off. I worked with my body thoroughly. I could show off with some impressive yoga acrobatics. I began to memorize *sutras* and learn to play the musical instruments used to accompany the chanting of Sanskrit texts. I worked hard at transformation and made a lot of progress. My Guru told me that transformation was like a bird with two wings: self-effort and grace. I knew self-effort. But I did not understand the part about grace.

I was living in the *ashram* (residential yoga center), studying at the feet of a Master. It was like being in the ocean while claiming that I was not getting wet. That was simply an impossibility. Every step of the way I was surrounded by grace. However, I never recognized it until I ran into my familiar brick wall. My self-effort frequently stranded me at a brick wall inside. Then I would begin to pray. Always, the answer came. Always, the grace was there. It took me a long time to see it when I was not in despair. It took even longer to learn to trust it.

Now, I know grace fills everything I do. It is a primary element of *Svaroopa Yoga*. All you have to do is get into the *asana* correctly, stay in it, surrender to the pose and then grace offers you something more. That something more is *svaroopa*, your own essence. It is given to you by grace. Without that, a pose is just more yoga acrobatics.

The *asana* is the way you position yourself to receive the gift of grace, which is freely given. You do not have to be good at the pose. You do not even have to be a worthy person. You do not even have to work for it. All you have to do is realize you are already in the ocean. You are getting wet with the flow of grace that surrounds and supports you.

There is also self-effort. My habitual style continues to be that of an achiever, but now my effort is applied toward finding and following the grace. Self-effort is best applied when you are looking at the grace.

Get in position. Look for the grace.

How Good Can it Get?

January 1995

I knew a man who drove a big truck. On the long stretches of road, he could not speed because of a device installed to hold him within the legal limit. That device was called a "governor." It held him back, for safety reasons. Most people have an internal governor that holds them back from their full experience of joy. Often a student will return after an absence of months, saying, "I never felt better than when I was coming to classes. I do not know why I stopped, but now I am back!" I know why they stopped. They ran into that governor.

Their life improved with yoga classes. They became healthier, stronger, more flexible, less stressed, and happier. Then, they stopped coming. Why? They could allow themselves to feel only so good. After that, they ran the risk of feeling too good, so they had to stop. Only after they lost it all did they realize what they had, and came back to find it again.

Yoga calls this "identification." It seems to be human nature to identify with your problems, your aches and pains, or your limitations. At the end of a recent class, a student said, "I do not know whose body this is. It does not feel like my own." "What is the difference?" I asked. She replied, "There is no pain." This means that her body is only her "own" if there is pain. If that pain was gone, whose body would she be living in?

Fortunately, yoga frees you. The problems, pains and seeming limitations dissolve steadily and reliably. But you must do it. It's just like a truck driver driving across the United States. You make headway toward the other coast as long as you drive for a certain number of hours each day. But if you stop driving, you go nowhere. Yoga will take you all the way, further than you can now imagine . . . But maybe it is okay with you to go only to the Midwest. It is your decision. Putting off the decision is a de facto decision.

> How long do you want to wait to feel good?
> How good do you want to feel?
> How good can you let it get?

Only you can answer these questions. Your answer is not given in words, but in action. Do more yoga.

PART II

෪

Daily Practice

Just Keep On
Keeping On

March 1996

"One of the simplest things about all facts of life is that to get where you want to go, you must keep on keeping on."

- Norman Vincent Peale

"The man who persists in knocking will succeed in entering."

- Moses Ibn Ezra

I confess that I have become accustomed to hearing inspiring stories. Students and teachers come to me every day with beautiful descriptions of how yoga has improved their life. The stories I hear are inspiring because they are true. Becoming accustomed to such a treat does not make the stories less meaningful. Instead, it deepens my trust in yoga itself, and makes me better able to answer the next person's questions with, "Just keep on keeping on. Keep on doing yoga and it will make the change you want."

This keeping on is *abhyasa* (perseverance) in Sanskrit. It is your ability to continue working on something in order to gain something greater. In fact, you get nothing in life unless you persevere. This is well known when it comes to getting a degree or a promotion. It is not as well understood when it comes to making a relationship work. In our modern world, perseverance is even less understood when it comes to personal growth or transformation. This is the age of the "quick fix," "instant gratification" and "more for less." We all have less time and money, with more to do and more pressure to get it all done. One of the greatest successes on Broadway may have gotten halfway there on the strength of its name alone, "Stop the World, I Want to Get Off!"

I remember finding my way to yoga. I wanted a quick fix. My life was working, sort of. Well, my life was okay, but it somehow wasn't enough. I had been looking around because I wanted something that would make a difference, and I wanted it NOW! It was a shock to realize how tight my body really was, and how un-peaceful my mind really was. But I did feel different at the end of my first class. Now, I love to help a new student feel welcome and to discover how good it feels after class. This is also true for a continuing student, but someone who has been "keeping on" for a while knows that yoga will produce this result every time, and that the result continues getting better.

Yoga does give you the "quick fix." It meets the "instant gratification" needs of the '90's. But yoga also offers more. I remember clearly, after I had been doing yoga for six months, I thought, "Wow! I have not hit the bottom of this well yet. There seems to be more here!" One day as I sat quietly in my room in India, I realized I had been doing full time yoga practices for six years. I thought, "Maybe this is a bottomless well." Now, more than twenty-five years after I began, I can truly say, "To think of it as a bottomless well would limit it. Yoga is more."

Spring is the time of year that students begin to fall away. So many yogis began classes right after New Year's, and were diligent in coming to class every week, or even two or three times each week. And now some of you are beginning to skip a class here and there. It reminds me of a student who returned about eight months ago. He told me, "I am so glad to be back. I came to classes here every week for about six months, and I felt better than I had ever felt in my life. Then I quit coming. That was two years ago. Now I realize that I quit coming because I did not think I should feel that good. I want you to know that I am back, and I am going to keep going this time." HOORAY! I celebrated his return with him. However, he came to class twice that week, once the next week, and he has not been back since. What happened?

You must cultivate the quality of perseverance. To continue to do yoga is to make the choice to feel good. In fact, you start to feel better than everyone around you. Every morning I greet the first few people of the day, and they say, "Hi, how are you?" I answer truthfully, "Great! How are you?" They answer that they are "Okay" or "Fine." What a shame. Are you ready to feel better than everyone around you? Then just keep doing yoga.

You make choices every day. As you are choosing what you will do, you are choosing how you will feel. When you choose to do something, you are setting up how you will feel, not only in the moment but also the next day. When you continue to do yoga, you will have inspiring stories to tell. You can be the next one who tells me an inspiring story, or maybe you will just have to live it. Do more yoga!

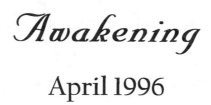

Awakening

April 1996

"*The spiritual journey does not consist in arriving at a new destination where a person gains what he did not have, or becomes grateful for what he is not ... The finding of God is a coming to one's self.*"

- Aldus Huxley

"*Our true nature does not have to be found; it is present at all times.*"

- Vernon Howard

The great sages of yoga tell us again and again, "Awake! Oh, my dear one, awaken from the dreams of your delusion." The ancient texts describe the ordinary events of life as temporary occurrences, like dreams. You get completely caught up in these events, forgetting the deeper essence inside. This inner essence is your true Self, which is the permanent aspect of your own existence. Yoga is a path of finding your true Self and then taking it into every event and relationship in your life. The yoga poses and yoga breathing are designed to give you an experience of your true Self, by clearing away what is blocking the way inside.

It is easy to mistake yoga poses for being a form of exercise. All the yoga practices, including the poses and the breathing, are very good for your body. But you are more than your body. Everyone who has ever fallen in love knows this. Everyone who wants to fall in love knows this as well, because we all want to be loved for something more than our bodies. We even want to be loved for something more than our minds. Everyone is actually running around looking for a way to experience that deeper essence by going to movies, concerts, taking vacations, through meaningful work and meaningful relationships. But the sages say, "Awake! Oh, my dear one. What you seek already lies inside."

Through yoga your body will improve. Your stress level will go down. You experience that inner essence even if it is just a momentary taste. The tools of yoga show you how to find that inner essence again and again.

When you slip inside, something happens. Something deep inside is awakened. You discover you are more than you previously thought yourself to be. And the way you live your life begins to change. If you do not want this awakening, go to the movies. If you want this awakening, practice yoga. You get to make that choice every day for the rest of your life.

Community

May 1996

"Without a sense of caring, there can be no sense of community."
- Anthony J. D'Angelo

"A scientific discovery is never the work of a single person."
- Louis Pasteur

A community of yogis growing, supporting and loving one another, and deepening our experience and commitment together is really something to celebrate!

When I began teaching in San Diego in 1987, I felt like I was alone in a crazy world. I had spent a lot of time living in India and in communities devoted to yoga as a spiritual quest. Our modern world seemed very foreign to me. I returned to a Western world that was caught up in the superficial aspects of yoga, trying to perfect the body by posing in beautiful yoga "poses." The yoga I knew focused on the spiritual aspects. I lived in a perpetual commitment to that higher goal. At first, I felt like a missionary, preaching how to use yoga's practices to find the deeper experience as well as how to apply yoga to life.

However, what happened is that I learned from all of you. What I learned was love. I learned to delight in each person who comes with their questions and their needs. We find a meeting ground that always reveals an underlying foundation of love. It is that foundation of love that sustains me and the service that all our teachers offer.

Creating Master Yoga Foundation was a big undertaking. It still is. We still stretch to balance the budget and fulfill our responsibilities. Our growing community is sometimes a support and sometimes a challenge. The growing base of charitable contributions makes a tremendous difference in our ability to continue our existing programs, as well as to expand them. It is easy for me to get caught up in the administrative needs of an organization this size, and forget the people that we serve. Fortunately, you won't let me. I thank you for that.

Every day someone calls with a question or a suggestion that changes my life. Every day someone stops me with their story of how yoga has helped them. Every day I am reminded of our growing sense of *unity* by a discussion with a staff member, teacher or student. There is an underlying foundation of unity that supports our *coming* together. It has redefined the meaning of the word *comm-unity* for me: coming together in unity. We can enjoy this in every class and every time we meet on the street. Community is an important form of yoga practice. Do more yoga!

34

The Path

June 1996

"In the spiritual life, all paths lead to the same place."

- Satchidananda

"The spiritual path is one of falling on your face, getting up, brushing yourself off, turning and looking sheepishly at God and then taking the next step."

- Shree Aurobindo

Yoga is a spiritual path that encompasses all the aspects of being human. *Hatha yoga* works with your body, *bhakti yoga* "exercises" your heart and *jnana yoga* stretches your mind. All give you the experience of transcendence. Whichever of the tools of yoga you are using, you are traveling "The Path." To talk about a path implies there is a beginning point and a destination. The destination is so important that you can get impatient that you are not there yet.

This happens when you are driving, too often in a rush to arrive at your destination. If the traffic signal takes too long or the freeway has become a parking lot, the drivers inch forward relentlessly. An opening appears and you race into it, only to fume when you have to stop again. Arriving, you are exhausted from the stress of the drive. There is a serious drawback to approaching life with this emphasis on the end result: The end result of life is death. Everything in between birth and death is a process. You must actually enjoy the ride, rather than fuming because you are not yet at your destination.

Personally, I love traffic jams. They make life so immediate! There is no future, because there is nowhere to go and no time in which I can plan to be "there." I put on music of my choice and sing along, or I do a few long yoga breaths *(ujjayi pranayama)*. I love that no one knows exactly where I am. I do not even have to be "who" I am. For a while all that stuff does not exist. When I arrive at my destination, I feel refreshed and rejuvenated. I had a good time.

The sages describe the spiritual path as one of becoming "realized." This means you do not go somewhere else, do something different, or become someone else; instead, you realize something that was always there. Currently, time seems to have a linear quality, with the past behind you and the future in front. However, you will realize there are other dimensions to time. This moment is not merely a point between past and future. There is a dimensionality to this moment that includes eternity. The spiritual path is the looking into that dimension. Then you learn to live in the multiple dimensions of your own existence all the time (except, of course, that time doesn't exist!).

Just as there is no destination on the spiritual path, there is no starting point. There is a point where you realize you have been on the path for some time. You may even begin to consciously cooperate with it. But when did it begin? Perhaps all of life is that spiritual path, and some people are cooperating with it while others resist it. You may even find that you do both.

The tools of yoga can help move you along the path when you are consciously cooperating with your own process of transformation. In addition, these tools are especially helpful when you are resisting, because that is when you most need the help. This is why sometimes the hardest part of yoga class is simply getting there. Once you get over that hump, everything else is easier.

The Goal

July 1996

"Life is not an end in itself.
Your goal is not conformed to this material world in which your body is
living. Your goal goes beyond this world of appearances. Your goal is
the attainment of Divine Perfection, which is the nature of absolute
peace and joy."

-Chidananda

"The goal of life is to become one with the Eternal . . .
You cannot reach the goal without leading a righteous life and without
possessing a pure heart."

-Sivananda

Yoga recommends that you set your goal at the highest attainment a human being can reach: being a fully enlightened being *in this lifetime.* To set your goal any lower is to settle for so much less that you can never truly be happy. All the other goals of life can be wonderful experiences, but without "Going for the Gold" of enlightenment, you would always feel that something is missing. However, yoga says you must also practice contentment, *samtosha.* How can you do both, to go for the highest and to be completely content when you have not yet attained it?

The secret is through understanding yoga's description of the goal of human life. What we call "full enlightenment" is a misnomer, better termed as "self-realized." Upon attaining the highest consciousness of which a human being is capable, every great Master has said that they realized they had always been Consciousness-and-Bliss. You do not become it. You already are it. The key is to simply realize it. The realized being describes his/her experience as a sublime and continuing experience of supreme contentment. Therefore, to practice contentment now is to place yourself already at your goal. However, there's a Catch 22. If you are content, will you continue to strive for the goal?

There must be a balance between your commitment to the goal and your contentment in the moment. You still must have the zeal that drives you forward into increasing levels of awareness and joy, while you have patience and self acceptance for the ways in which you are not yet enlightened. You need unwavering focus on your goal, while you enjoy compassion and camaraderie with the others who share the path with you. A great teacher once said that you must let go of all desires on the path to enlightenment, except one. You're allowed to keep your desire for enlightenment itself . . . but only until the last moment. Then, you must let go of even that desire, or it will keep you from seeing that you already are the Self. You need only realize that you are already Consciousness-and-Bliss. Until then, practice contentment. Or simply do more yoga.

Cause & Effect

August 1996

*"A human being fashions his consequences
as surely as he fashions his goods or his dwelling.
Nothing he says, thinks, or does is without consequences."*

- Norma Cousins

"The seed never explains the flower."

- Edith Hamilton

CR

As the days draw closer to our upcoming Yoga Retreat, I feel a "sweetening" in the air. It seems that even the air in the yoga rooms is getting ready to welcome the yogis who will be diving deeply into yoga, which includes those who are coming for the Retreat as well as those who will simply continue with regular yoga classes. The power of the Retreat creates an effect that spreads to everyone who gets here for even one class. And that effect is already beginning to build.

Yoga describes this as the law of *karma*, which we experience as the law of *cause and effect*. When you take yoga classes, it has an effect on your life. Yoga's reliable effects include feeling physically better (or even relief of pain), becoming more flexible (body and mind), having less accumulated stress, being less reactionary to life events (calmer), etc. *Cause*: taking yoga classes—*Effect*: improvement in your life. More than this, each person who takes yoga is the cause of improvement in the lives of those around them as well. Several years ago, a student brought a friend to class. The student shared, "I have only taken three classes, and I have changed so much!" Her friend piped up, "Yes, she is nicer now." Fortunately, the student agreed with her friend's assessment. *Cause*: Taking yoga classes—*Effect*: Improvement in your life and lives of those around you.

In addition, every time you come to yoga, you benefit from all the other people who have been coming. This group energy is real. It is the reason that you may go further into the poses and deeper into the relaxation when you are in class compared to doing poses at home. Yoga rooms have a different feel to them even when there is no one there. This is also *karma*, for the people who have done yoga in these rooms have created an effect in the room itself. *Cause*: More yoga being done by more people—*Effect*: People feel even better when they do yoga in the place devoted to yoga practices.

How far can this go? These retreats include a wide variety of yoga practices from 7 to 9 p.m. every day FOR 23 DAYS. Participants have a yearning to deepen their experience of yoga. Many of them also want to share it with others by becoming yoga teachers. It is a pure pleasure to welcome such inspiring and enthusiastic yogis, and to stand with them on the threshold of an exciting adventure.

You are all invited to enjoy the effect of their *karma* (which literally means "action"). *Cause*: The Retreat Participants immerse themselves in yoga practices—*Effect*: Everyone gets more benefits in yoga classes. If you cannot join us in the Retreat, you can benefit from their deepening into yoga. You can ride on their coattails. Then you will automatically spread the effects of yoga into the world through the way it changes your life.

The Luminous Flame of Being

September 1996

"As far as we can discern, the sole purpose of human existence is to kindle a light in the darkness of mere being."

- Carl Jung

"Light is the symbol of truth."

- James Russell Lowell

This month, we welcome many who are dedicated to the luminous flame of being. Along with new and returning students, we welcome two neighboring organizations who share a dedication to spreading this light of being in the world, The Chopra Center and La Jolla Pain Treatment Center. Actually, it is impossible to spread this Light, because it is already there. It is already everywhere. What Master Yoga does, and what our new neighbors also do, is to help people become aware that the Luminous Flame of Being exists inside. It is the source of all bliss, all healing, all joy and all love.

In a yoga class, it is easy to get distracted and think that it is all about mastering a yoga pose, or tying yourself up in a pretzel shaped knot. Likewise, when dealing with health issues, it's easy to get distracted into thinking that you're treating a body part or solving a problem. Our new neighbors agree that you must treat the whole person, and to bring them inexorably closer to knowing the luminous flame of their own being. All healing comes from this source, and yoga's tools make it easy to connect with that inner source again. The tools of yoga can really help with the backache, headache and stress level, as well as many major illnesses.

For those of you who have no health problems, you do not have to hurt before you practice yoga. We guarantee bliss! *Svaroopa Yoga* is so reliable that it is easy to make this guarantee. So, if you hurt and you want to feel better — come to yoga. If you do not hurt and you want to feel better — come to yoga. If you feel good and you want to feel better — come to yoga! Do more yoga.

Contentment

October 1996

*"When we cannot find contentment in ourselves,
it is useless to seek it elsewhere."*

-Francois La Rochefoucauld

*"The best way to lead a peaceful life is to be content with the situation in
which God places us. We seek changes and the result is we get into a
worse hole than the previous one."*

-Papa Ramdas

To practice contentment might make you a disruptive element in our modern world. Yoga names contentment, *samtosha*, as a primary practice. But, the everyday influences of society propel you to an endless stream of desires. All you have to do is watch one television show, and your "Discontent Factor" increases. It is not the shows themselves as much as it is the ads. They are exceptionally effective at stimulating your desires, which makes you more and more dis-content. Yoga makes you content.

I remember the first time I felt content. I was sitting in my bedroom in a yoga *ashram* (residential yoga center), and I realized I felt strange. Something was missing on the inside. Something familiar was gone, and I did not feel quite like the "me" that I had known for so many years. But I did not know what it was. I cast about, looking for what was missing, and could not find it. So, I tried instead to describe to myself more specifically how I was feeling. Finally, I realized that I felt content. That scared me! While it felt so good to feel such deep contentment, I instantly felt fear that I would never strive for anything again. I realized that all the activities of my life had been motivated by a deep discontent, and now it was gone. It seemed that there was no reason to do anything, ever again.

It took days of feeling contentment before I realized that I could (and would) still do everything there is do, but it would be for a different reason. I became free from need, at least for a short time. Everything I did was done out of joy; there was not even a twinge of need in it. It did not matter if what I was doing "succeeded" or "failed." It was fine either way.

The ancient sages describe contentment as a high attainment that arises spontaneously through continued yoga practice. They also recommend contentment as a practice, schooling your mind and applying your will to foster an inner contentment no matter what is going on around you. This is definitely different than the way society directs you. If you want to be a revolutionary, practice yoga. If you want to change the way life is lived in this modern age, practice yoga. At least your life will change — and maybe the world around you will, too.

Gratitude

November 1996

"*A grateful thought toward Heaven is itself a prayer.*"

-Rudolph Block

"*A thankful heart is not only the greatest virtue,*
but the parent of all other virtues."

-Cicero

It is so appropriate that the Holiday Season begins with a day of Thanks. We can get so lost in the gift-giving and all the preparations for the big December Day, that we rarely stop to appreciate what we already have. More than merely "appreciate," this is a time to feel and express gratitude. To express your thanks is one of the easiest ways to melt your heart. To feel grateful is to pause in a moment of sweet surrender. This surrender is an essential part of yoga. More importantly, it is an important part of life.

Everyone longs for the experience of surrender, whether through seeking a soulmate or by learning to scuba dive. That experience of overwhelm is an extraordinary letting go of all the tricks we usually use to isolate ourselves. Yoga says, "Just let go!" Let yourself be overwhelmed by the beauty of the moment. Give over to the majesty of the space between the ticks of the clock.

Gratitude is one of the best ways to do this. Begin with saying "Thank you" to your own body. It has carried you so far and given you so many experiences. Even if it is not perfect, look at what it does for you every day. So often we have only complaints about the body. We focus on the spot that hurts, or complain that we don't look like the model in the magazine. It is a foreground-background thing. Shift your gaze from the ache or pain to the background: the whole rest of your body. Like when you are at the beach, you can watch a sailboat cross the horizon, or you can widen your gaze to include the whole scene with the ocean, sky and boat. Widen your awareness to your whole body, which includes the "problem area." Speak out loud (or at least in a whisper) and say "Thank you" to your body. Then, look around to find something else to be grateful for, and speak up again. Do one more, so you do at least three. Once you get started, you may have difficulty stopping. It is like eating one potato chip, except it usually takes three to get the gratitude going.

Now do it again. "Thank you, body for . . . (fill in the blank)." And add two more thank you's to the list. Notice how you feel.

This is yoga for the mind, mental *asanas*. Practice daily and it will change your life. I will close with three of my own:

- *Thank you, body, for all the bliss (and all the lessons).*
- *Thank you to the one who has given me this body and this life.*
- *Thank you to you, the reader, for giving me the opportunity to offer myself, through yoga and through these words.*

The Bliss of Pure Being

December 1996

*"Enlightenment is simply waking up
and recognizing the illusion of life for what it is."*

-Shantidasa

*"There are many paths to enlightenment.
Be sure to take the one with a heart."*

-Lao-tzu

What got me into yoga was the bliss. I dabbled in yoga for a time, watching yoga television, clipping magazine articles, even buying some books. I would do yoga once and then leave it alone for a while. I realize now that it was because I was a couch-potato in the making. My three young children kept me from lying around, but I was destined for the couch-potato hall of fame. I was not into exercise. Then I found out about bliss.

Actually, I already knew about bliss. We all do. But we seek our bliss indirectly. I had tried many avenues to bliss, especially in the '60's and '70's, but found they only worked part of the time. Some of them had damaging side effects. Some of them were even illegal. When I found the bliss that yoga offers, I was hooked. It has been a most beneficial addiction.

The first yoga class I took was not blissful. I found things in my body that I did not want to admit were there. I thought it was the teacher's fault that these things hurt so much. I did not go back. A different teacher put me in touch with the bliss of yoga. I realized it was what I had been looking for in all the other things I tried in my life. This is why I teach Bliss Yoga. Now, I consider myself a specialist in bliss.

December is a time of year when we all become more open to the inner dimension. We complain when commercialization distracts us from that potential. We know that something gets lost. That something is something we really want. It is a human need. If there is too little bliss in your life, you begin to feel there is no reason to live. Yoga will help you with that. Do more yoga.

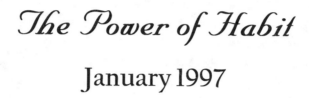

The Power of Habit

January 1997

"Men's natures are alike; it is their habits that carry them far apart."
- Confucious

"We are what we repeatedly do.
Excellence then, is not an act, but a habit."

- Aristotle

It is that time of year again. You make plans to establish better habits. New Year's Resolutions are one of our most important rituals. From yoga's point of view, making resolutions is a form of self-knowledge as well as a commitment to becoming something greater. You have to know yourself well enough to acknowledge that it is time to make a change. And you are able to create (at least in your mind) a different view of yourself. Thus, you see some of the places where you are stuck, and you know what you need to do. You make a "Resolution." Making the resolution "stick" is the problem.

It is actually very easy to establish new habits. You need only do your "new thing" for three days in a row. This is easy to understand if you consider how this works with an indulgence. Let us say that you go out for a hot fudge sundae at 2 p.m. every day for three days in a row. The fourth day at 2 p.m., you would have an irresistible craving for a hot fudge sundae. Good habits are actually just as easy to establish.

One of the keys to keeping your resolutions is to set them up in a way that you actually enjoy following through. Every January, we welcome many students to yoga classes. Some of you are new to yoga and some are returning. You are more likely to keep attending if you like yoga, or if you like the way you feel at the end of your yoga classes. Fortunately, that is one of the most reliable things about *Svaroopa Yoga*. In fact, we wish that every day you would feel like you feel after a yoga class. The important thing is to remember that you can get it back again when you lose it.

Put yoga in your New Year's Resolutions. Or you can consider it as making a promise to yourself, if the word "resolution" is too scary. Take advantage of the New Year energy to make those changes you know you need (and that you really want). You could even come to a class three days in a row and see how good you could feel.

Kindness

February 1997

"To cultivate kindness is a valuable part of the business of life."

- Samuel Johnson

"Kindness means doing a lot of little things kindly and always, not just big things now and then."

- Neville Hobson

"Do unto others as you would have them do unto you." I thought I lived by the Golden Rule until I began to understand yoga's teaching, "Honor the other person, for they are a spark of divine consciousness, as you are." Then, I realized that I had always followed the Golden Rule as though it said, "Be nice to others, so they will be nice to you." I wanted other people to be nice to me, and being nice to them was a way to get what I wanted. Sometimes it worked. Sometimes I just became a doormat for other people.

When I realized this, I stopped being nice. All those years of being nice had been an act, anyway. Now my real personality began to show. I was rude and abrupt. I would smile, but it was not genuine. On the occasions that I forced myself to slow down and be nice, I felt superior to the incredibly dense and slow person I was dealing with, so I would be nice out of pity. Amazingly, there were still people who liked me. There were a lot who did not, but I did not care. The problem was that I was not happy. Even though I was not a phony any more, I had to live with a rude, abrupt person — myself.

I further considered yoga's teaching and made a real effort to see the other person as divine consciousness. Since I lived in an *ashram* (residential yoga center) during this time, the people who surrounded me were all working on themselves. But they were far from enlightened beings. At least it seemed that way to me. Keep in mind that it is always easier to see how someone else is unenlightened than to see it in yourself. I would sit and think of a person I really disliked and contemplate, "Somewhere inside you is a spark of divine consciousness, even if I cannot see it yet."

I began treating other people better. Over time it got easier. It became a habit to look for that spark in each person. As I have continued this practice over the years, it continued to change. I began to really see that spark in everyone. More than that, even the unenlightened parts began to look like a manifestation of divine consciousness. Now, I need few reminders to greet each person with true welcome and joy. Quite naturally, I have become genuinely friendly and kind. Even when I have to speak up strongly or move quickly, people tell me they experience compassion or kindness in what I do. Perhaps it is because yoga has made me able to see God in each one of you. Thank you for being in my life.

❧

Service

March 1997

"The purpose of life is to increase the warm heart. Think of other people. Serve other people sincerely. No cheating."

-Dalai Lama

"The most acceptable service of God is doing good to man."

-Benjamin Franklin

To offer your service to others is one of the most powerful and sweetest of yoga's practices. However, society urges you to serve your desires. The stresses of today come from a relentless pursuit of desires, as though you can only attain true and long lasting happiness when you acquire everything you desire. Yoga says that the desires must desert you in order for you to find the happiness you seek, because the desires themselves block the source of happiness which is inside. The desires are like a black coating on a light bulb, eclipsing the light of consciousness which shines from the inside out.

You must learn to live your daily life in a different way. The health and vitality offered by the practice of yoga poses and breathing is only the beginning. Yoga reconnects you to the inner realms of consciousness to make you feel whole again. But those moments of connectedness are not enough if the activities of life draw you away again. Life itself must become "yogified." The yoga practice of service teaches you how.

Service is one of the most profound practices of yoga, and one of the least known. It has been a well kept secret at Master Yoga since we began. Master Yoga has been built on the loving service of so many, and continues to grow and thrive because of their continuing loving service. *Karma yoga* is one of the names given to this practice. This means that you offer your efforts (*karma*) without any repayment or return. This is not the yoga of exercise or meditation, it is the yoga of work. My favorite term for this is *seva*. *Seva* means "selfless service," giving of yourself unselfishly.

This used to be called "volunteer work." In our age of beepers and organizers, few people prioritize *seva* in their schedule. Yet, life without *seva* is barren. Anyone who has ever participated in creating Christmas for a destitute family, shared the daily tasks of the local schoolroom or painted the church dining hall knows the true joy that comes from simply showing up to do what needs to be done. You cannot paint your own dining room and feel the same way. Something comes from the giving of your time, effort and love that comes in no other way.

I feel that I am among the most blessed of people because I have been able to offer my work as *seva* for more than fourteen of the last twenty years. I know the truth of the saying, "*Seva* gives you everything" and invite you to find out for yourself. Find some place to offer yourself in the yoga of service.

ॐ

April 1997

"*One joy scatters a hundred griefs.*"

- Chinese Proverb

"*To get the full value from joy you must have someone to divide it with.*"

-Mark Twain

Joy is the substratum of your being and the foundation of all of existence. You experience this every time it bubbles to the surface. You even look for things in your life that will allow it to bubble up. In these moments you say that you are "happy." I wish for you that your life be filled with many of them. I wish for you that the inner veil of separation between the outside and your essence be very thin, so this inner joy can bubble up for the slightest of reasons.

The world is a physical manifestation of joy. It shows in the exuberance of a flower, especially one that is still on the plant. Look at it and see how it is so alive and so joyful. If you watch puppies or kittens, you naturally begin to smile or laugh. Yesterday at Seal Beach, I saw a baby seal beside its mom. They laid together on the sand and the baby began to nurse. All the people standing nearby were pointing and grinning. This joy seems to be contagious; it is almost like germs. Actually it's not contagious; what happens is that an event makes you able to let go and experience the joy which is always inside you.

The heads of all the people in a restaurant turn to watch the little tyke toddling through. Someone carries a baby into the room and everyone watches. A few people indulge themselves and go over to say "Hi." They smile and their whole body relaxes. Others hang back because that inner veil of separation is too thick. They cannot let it down for such a small reason. Something really big has to happen before they let themselves be filled with happiness.

Consider that you were once the baby or toddler that sparked other people's joy. Now, however, you see other people's faces and you experience something other than joy. You focus on your expectations and desires, or you replay old memories of not-joyful times. You are actually focusing your attention on the inner veil of separation, rather than looking through it to the joy inside.

The practices of yoga thin the inner veil of separation. Yoga offers practices to open the upwelling of joy inside. Then, you can carry that feeling with you wherever you go. The littlest things can then stimulate the familiar surge of joy, because the veil is thinner. In this way your life becomes full of joy, not because the outside is perfect, but because the inside is. It's called yoga.

Greatness

May 1997

*"One in All. All in One-if only this is realized.
No more worry about your not being perfect."*

- Seng-ts'an

*"If any man seeks for greatness,
let him forget and ask for the trusth, and he will find both."*

- Horace Mann

I was awakened at 5 a.m. by the phone ringing. It was a friend who was on retreat at a yoga ashram (residential yoga center) in a time zone three hours ahead of my own. She said, "My *Guru* told me to call you and tell you, 'You Are Great!'" My heart stopped. I was thrust into a different Reality. My mind struggled for footing as if on a slippery path. I stammered, "Wh-wh-what?!" She said again, "I'm supposed to tell you, 'You Are Great!'" Then I got it. My life changed in that moment and it never went back. I later found out that over 2,000 people attended that early morning program and made those phone calls. My friend tells me today, three years later, that she knew it was a personal command to her — to make a personal call to me.

I wish for you that you know that this is a personal message for you: YOU ARE GREAT! (Pause.) (Take a deep breath.) (Repeat to yourself, "I Am Great!'). You are great — not because of what you do, not because of whom you know, and not because of where you go. You are great because you are. The problem underlying the stress and unhappiness you experience in life is that you think yourself to be small. In yoga, this is called "ego." You think and feel yourself to be small and that you must *do* something to become great. Actually, you cannot *become* great. You are already great — as you are.

The ego is a function of your mind, which attempts to pare you down to size, as though it were cutting you away from Consciousness-Absolute. Thus you feel that you are individual, separate and alone. Actually, you are both part of consciousness and you have the whole of consciousness within you. It is like your body and your cells: each cell is part of your body, yet each cell has the whole of your DNA in it and could (theoretically) be cloned into another body identical to yours. In a similar way you are part of God's creation, while you are also "made in God's image," with the whole blueprint of consciousness complete within you. To know it, you only need to remember — or to be reminded of it by an early morning phone call or an article or book — YOU ARE GREAT!

Your job in life is to find and know this essence of greatness, then to pour it into your life. Do not ask your life to make you great. Instead, pour your greatness into every task, every conversation, and every relationship with every person — because every other person is also that same Greatness that you are. Whether they look at the Greatness that is their own essence or not, you can. This is the secret of life. This is the goal of yoga. This is the meaning of yoga's greeting, *"Namaste,"* I honor the Greatness that is your true identity, from the Greatness that is my Self.

Discipline

June & July 1997

"Most powerful is he who has himself in his own power."

- Seneca

*"Discipline is the ability to carry out a resolution
long after the mood has left you."*

- Susan Smith Jones

You uncover the greatness within by doing something every day to bring if forth. It is what you do every day that matters. If you watch the television news every day, you will be very well informed, but you will not uncover the greatness within. If you do some yoga every day, that greatness brightens daily. It is incredible. It is reliable. You can prove it to yourself very easily. Just do ten to twenty minutes of yoga every day for three days, and then skip a day. For three days you will become increasingly more cheerful, friendlier to others, less stressed, more clear headed, and your body will feel better. Watch what happens on the day you skip, as you backslide to what everyone calls "normal."

Yoga gives you the ability to choose how you want to feel. You can redefine normal. Normal actually means you fit in with the norm. Unfortunately, the norm is stressed and unhappy, with a high level of frustration in daily life. Many people start yoga classes because of this, hoping that yoga will make them feel better. It does! And it does much more. It is immediately obvious that your body gets better, but so does everything else. You will keep your same family, and the same house, job and car, while you become happier and more effective in all of them. Because when you do yoga, you see them all differently. You even see yourself differently. Your old normal changes into something quite wonderful. For this you must have discipline.

Yoga only works when you do it. It is like your television, which only works when you turn it on. You have to do yoga in order to get the benefits. However, if you merely think about yoga, it is actually still beneficial. Just remembering the feeling after that final relaxation in yoga class will give you a taste of the same feeling again. But it will fade quickly unless you do something more.

You get nothing in your life without discipline. You can't buy a home or get a college degree without discipline. You cannot even hold a job without discipline. Everything of value comes from applying yourself again and again, and the results improve over time. Yoga is the same. If you find a time to integrate some yoga poses into your daily schedule, like ten minutes in the morning or fifteen minutes before you go to bed, you will get immediate and lasting benefit.

Discipline means that you do it regularly. The full discipline of yoga is to do it every day. But you can consider yourself to be disciplined if you do it every other day, or twice a week, or even only once a week. It is the regularity that makes the difference. And next year, when you have been doing your daily discipline for a year, you will actually get more benefit from the same amount of time invested.

It is a law of increasing returns. If you could do this with your bank account or the gas tank of your car, you would not hesitate. You would sign up immediately. How about if you get these increasing returns for your body, for your mind, and for your life? Do more yoga.

Freedom

August 1997

"Freedom: There's none unless you know the Self.
But if you know the truth, then you are free."

-The Upanishads

"Wherever the spirit of God is, there is freedom."

-Paul of Tarsus

The goal of yoga is "Liberation." It means you can completely transcend the normal human condition described as "Bondage." Any time that you feel that you must have certain people or certain things surrounding you, you are bound to them. Worse than that, you feel incomplete unless you have these external validations of your identity and value. Yoga offers freedom, which means that it makes you feel complete and whole without external crutches to prop up your identity. Yoga's goal of freedom points to a deep and profound level of human experience, which can be reached on either of two yoga paths.

On one path you can create this freedom by eliminating all your attachments. Your attachments are the people and things you rely on to create a temporary sense of self. This temporary sense of self changes when your situation changes, like when you leave work and go home, or when you go out with friends and feel like a completely different person than when you attend your evening college class. Some of your attachments may be so strong that they qualify as dependencies or even addictions, but all must be eliminated. On this path, you may even decide to change where you work and who you know. But you must be careful to not replace them with new attachments. This path to freedom is the path of renunciation. In this path you continually renounce everything that creates a temporary sense of self until you can find the real unchanging Self inside.

I confess that I prefer the other path — yoga's path of bliss. You use yoga's practices for the purpose of finding the deeper dimension of being, so that you feel filled from the inside. As you become more accustomed to feeling full and whole, you take this feeling with you into your work and home. You begin to carry this new sense of self wherever you go. You become able to enjoy all aspects of your life without depending on them. In this path you find the deeper Self and practice staying in it until the old distracting "small selves" simply dissolve away.

The end result of either path is a tremendous sense of freedom, because you remain full and complete no matter what is happening on the outside. With this freedom comes a great love and respect for everyone and everything else, because you see that all are amazing and wonderful expressions of the same Source, which you have found inside your own being. This is *yoga*, "union."

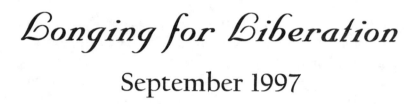

Longing for Liberation

September 1997

"Unless you fulfill this longing, you will always feel only partially alive."

- Rama Berch

I always loved to sing the blues. It was the only way I could express a deep, unnamed yearning that had been there all my life. There were no other words for it until I found yoga. Yoga calls it *mumukshitva*, which means the longing for liberation. It was a constant companion through all my life. Now I call it a friend, but for many years it seemed to be the root of all my suffering. Everything I did was an attempt to get rid of it. Joseph Campbell told Bill Moyers in a television interview, "Everyone experiences it, but not everyone acts on it." When I heard this, I was shocked. My immediate response was, "How can you *not* act on it? It's so painful!"

We all experience this longing. From birth to age two, we learned how to handle our body, including how to walk and talk. From age two to seven, we asked and answered the question, "How do I handle the objects in the world?" We mastered how to butter toast, draw on paper, etc. From age seven to puberty, we explored how to interact with others in games, in groups, as friends and as enemies. At puberty a new question arose, "Is this it? Isn't there something more?" This was the beginning of the spiritual quest, and the source of adolescent angst. Our society avoided this question and all its possible answers, so we were left in a painful limbo. We tried the old things more intensely: more things to do with our bodies (sports), more things to do with objects in the world (shopping, music, etc.), more things to do in relationship (social activities). The more adventurous (or the more desperate) of us tried out some answers that were taboo. "Sex, drugs and rock-and-roll" are a dead-end street, but sometimes you have to try every avenue.

This feeling is a spiritual longing, a deep desire to know the truth of your own being. You have been taught to repress this spiritual longing through abusing your body, climbing the corporate ladder, and the unending crusade to maintain your fading youth and beauty. Yoga says that this longing is the life in you. Unless you fulfill this longing, you will always feel only partially alive. Yoga not only acknowledges and names this feeling, but it has thousands of ways of fulfilling it. This is why the first line of Master Yoga's three-fold statement of purpose is, "*cultivating our innate yearning for transcendence.*"

In every yoga class, you will get to stretch, breathe and relax. You need never go any further. Yet, this begins to feed you at some deep nameless level. When you leave you feel like yourself again. I invite you to contemplate the inherent yearning that has been there all your life long. Look into it, and you may find your true Self.

Creating Personal Experiences of the Inner Truth

October 1997

"To live in this experience all the time, you need only see God literally.
Your greatest mistake is that you think of God as acting symbolically
and allegorically rather than practically and literally. Get rid of the idea
trhat you have yet to realize the truth of your own being.
You are that here and now. Who do you sense yourself to be?"

-Paraphrased from Ramana Maharshi

"This, above all, to thine own self be true."

-William Shakespeare

The second line in Master Yoga's Statement of Purpose is, *"creating personal experiences of the Inner Truth."* Yoga has 100,000 ways to create an experience of Inner Truth and even a larger variety of names for it. One of my favorite names is *ananda* (bliss), but I hear many other names from you. Recent comments I have heard from students include:

> *"The most immediate effect of yoga is the inner calm, the state of acceptance of what-is, and deeper levels of letting go. The most obvious effect is peacefulness."*
>
> *"Yoga makes me feel equanimity and realize oneness."*
>
> *"All the clouds in my head clear away and I know who I am when I do yoga."*

The ancient texts validate these descriptions, but yoga is not found in a stack of old dusty books. It is ancient but not antiquated. It is old but not stale. The *Shiva Sutras* describe the experience of yoga as *iccha shaktir uma-kumari* — the inner experience feels ancient and ever new. It is your own experience of the ancient source of all existence, yet it feels ever new. The experience places you in an inner realm where time does not exist. It is full of joy, like the enthusiasm of a child on Christmas morning. It never wears out. Bliss never gets boring.

This experience is alive in everyone and can be found with an easy yoga pose, a long breath, or a moment of remembrance. But if your yearning is weak, anything can distract you. You will forget to use the tools of yoga to create a deeper satisfaction. It is too easy to get lost in the events around you. You end up pursuing things which (at first) seem to be wonderful, but then you discover that they provide you with only temporary bliss or that they come with a lot of drawbacks.

The practice of yoga creates reliable inner experiences that get deeper, richer and more delicious, that last longer each time. Then, your life is filled with bliss even when outside conditions are not exactly perfect. You can create that experience for yourself when you are not in yoga class. You must remember this Inner Truth, and do something to get back to it. Be kind to your own Inner Truth. Remember to remember!

Discovering this as a Continuing Experience in our Lives

November & December 1997

"Yoga promises that you can have this experience,
and calls it by many names, including 'realization.'"

- Rama Berch

This is the third element of the Master Yoga Foundation's Statement of Purpose, as well as the true goal of yoga. I have been exploring each of these statements. First you discover your inherent longing for the inner experience. Then, you create personal experiences of it. Now, you can consider living in it all the time! Yoga promises that you can live this way and calls it by many names, including "realization."

You may not have been planning on becoming a realized being in this lifetime…it is really your choice. But if you consider the alternative, you might get interested. Without moving toward realization, what direction are you going? Begin by considering what your habitual mood is. Everyone has one. It even gets etched into your face after enough years of wearing it. How do you feel when you first wake in the morning? Maybe you are one of those people that we shouldn't talk to for the first hour or until you have had your morning coffee. What is going on inside you that you need that "fix?"

When my children were growing up, one was impossibly cheerful in the morning, awakening with an incredible joy everyday. At first it was just irritating; then it became a concern to me because it seemed abnormal. Now I realize that it truly was abnormal, because the norm is something much less happy. Life seems to promise diminishing returns, particularly at the age that the Baby Boomers are reaching now. It cannot be that life is so limiting. There must be something more. Yoga says that there is!

Just behind the part of your mind that you usually look at is another dimension of your own being. When you look in this direction, you find a joy that does not rely on circumstances. You "realize" that you have always been something greater than you thought. Thus, you become a "realized" being. It means you have found yourself. The alternative is to feel lost. You already know how that feels.

It does not happen all at once. For most people, it comes in stages. First, you take a few yoga classes so that you feel better. Then, you may find that you don't get stressed as easily. You keep studying, practicing, and even read a few yoga books. You learn a new way of setting priorities. You apply a few of yoga's tricks (like a slow, long breath) whenever you notice that you are getting lost in the events unfolding around you. The peace and joy of yoga begin to carry with you everywhere you go, and bit by bit it draws you closer to realization. You have to do your part, but it is easy because yoga always works.

You might be one of those who are in a rush to get to realization. I was. But as the stages develop, you begin to feel so good that there is no reason to rush any more. You can trust yoga's promise that you will know yourself — you will live in that continuing experience all the time. Just take it one step at a time and yoga guarantees it!

Creating Conscious Community
& Offering Service

January & February 1998

*"Once we discover we have a yearning for an inner experience
and act upon it, then we want to find others
who have the same priorities in their life."*

- Rama Berch

We have been guided by our Statement of Purpose since our founding almost six years ago. It has been a constant inspiration to me and its meaning deepens with each reading. We open and close all Master Yoga meetings with a contemplation on it. I have featured it as the theme for the last few articles. Yet, it has long seemed incomplete because we were always doing more than what the original three lines named.

It is a delight to unveil the addition of two new lines. This is truly an unveiling, because it is a new understanding of what has always existed. In this way it is truly yoga, which the sages describe as the unveiling of the Inner Truth that was always there but was unrecognized! Our Statement of Purpose has been:

> *Cultivating our innate yearning for transcendence,*
> *Creating personal experiences of the Inner Truth,*
> *Discovering this as a continuing experience in our lives,*

Now, we add these two lines:

> *Applying this in the development of conscious community,*
> *Offering our service to support and uplift humanity.*

Once we discover that we have a yearning for an inner experience and act upon it, then we want to find others who have the same priorities in their lives. Spending time in the company of other yogis is an important and powerful part of the process. It can be hard to develop friendships when everyone in your yoga class is silent and then floats out afterward in a state of deep quietude. Sometimes you don't even know whether or not to say, "Hi!" But you have the opportunity to meet the nicest people in a yoga class.

In addition, our teachers ask questions during class designed to do two things: foster greater self-understanding and create an opening for conversations that students can follow up on later. This gives you an opportunity to consciously create community with other conscious people.

Just as the inner experience naturally overflows into your relationships, it then becomes an upwelling of a desire to serve. This is the most fulfilling of all activities and is a yoga unto itself, *karma yoga*. It is our pleasure to serve you by offering yoga programs. When your activities come from the place in you that has been filled by yoga, it makes you more able to serve others in your life. We look forward to seeing you and serving you.

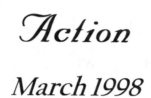

Action

March 1998

"Never confuse movement with action."

- Ernest Hemingway

"If the fruits of action do not affect the person, he is free."

- Ramana Maharshi

CR

Modern life defines our activity level. When you do more, you are worth more, or at least you are a more interesting person. Life can be so overbooked that you have to come to yoga in order to relax. You hurry up to get here so that you can lie down on the floor and do nothing. Yoga seems to say, "Slow down!" The slowing down is a complete halt in the relaxation at the beginning of a class. It is truly needed, but for a different reason than you might expect. There is nothing wrong with activity. There is nothing wrong with the amount of activities you engage in, or with the things you choose to do. The problem arises from your reasons for doing those activities.

Yoga will change the reasons that you do things. I began yoga with the desire to be free from pain, both physical pain as well as a deep obscure pain that was impossible to put into words. That pain was the motivation for everything I did, whether I recognized it or not. I worked hard and I played hard to avoid feeling that pain. I continued my education in hopes of getting ahead, convinced that success would alleviate the pain. I embarked upon relationships in order to get free from the constant gnawing inside. I did all the things that society recommended, but none of it gave me what I really wanted. I finally turned it all upside down and dove into yoga because it worked. The deeper I got into yoga the more effective it was. This is still true over twenty-five years later.

Now, I do all the things I was running away from when I escaped to India. I work hard. I take great vacations. I have meaningful relationships and am enjoying an unanticipated level of success. But I do it all for a different reason than before. Activity itself has not gone away. Sometimes my daily schedule is far more challenging than life was "before yoga." But I am not doing these things in order to be free from pain. I am not waiting for someone else to acknowledge me or need me. I feel joyful inside and the joy overflows into activity. The activities of my day arise from an inner fullness that supports me, rather than an emptiness that seeks to be filled.

When you begin yoga practice, you must create times where all activity stops. It is not because yoga values inactivity. It is because you need quiet time in order to find the essential piece that was getting overlooked: your Self. You have this tendency to identify with what you do, including your profession as well as your hobbies. Yoga gives you something else to identify with —

Consciousness-Itself, which is your true Self. In the midst of life, take a moment to consider the motivations for your actions. Then, look beyond your actions, and beyond your reasons. Find a way to remember the true Self in the midst of activity. This is the yoga of life.

Karma

April 1998

"*For every action, there is an equal and opposite reaction. If you push hard on the world. the world pushes back on you. If you touch the world gently, the world will touch you gently in return.*"

-Paul Hewitt

"*A human being fashions his consequences as surely as he fashions his goods or his dwelling. Nothing that he says, thinks, or does is without consequences.*"

-Norman Cousins

People only ask me about *karma* when they are having difficulties. They want to know about *karma* because they do not like theirs. Nobody ever asks me about *karma* when they are enjoying the fruits of life. When things are not going well, however, you do not really have the right to complain about bad *karma* because you actually gave it to yourself. *Karma* is the results of your past actions coming back to haunt (or bless) you.

If you do not like your *karma*, change it! How do you do this? Simply do the things you've already heard about: work diligently, live a disciplined and pure life, treat other people well, volunteer your time and give donations to charity, think positively, etc. Yoga's advice is amazingly similar to what you heard from your parents. Yet yoga offers something more because it actually makes this advice easier to follow. When you do yoga, all of these important things become easier to put into practice.

From yoga's point of view, *karma* is superficial and (mostly) unimportant. More important is your continued yoga practice, for it gives you the ability to maintain a joyous equilibrium regardless of what is going on in your life. In other words, your *karma* will not bother you. You already know what this is like if you have taken even one yoga class, because you know that you feel differently afterwards, even if your life is not perfect. Your capacity to deal with your *karma* changes when you do yoga — and so does your *karma*, because you naturally and easily begin to live your life more in accordance with that list of how to improve your life.

Do more yoga, have less *karma*!

Joyfulness

May 1998

"You are a fountain of joy."

— Shankaracharya

"Joy is not in things, it is in us."

— Charles Wagner

CR

Joy is your true nature, rather than merely an emotion or feeling. It is your divine inheritance, to which you are entitled as a birthright. There is nothing that you need do to earn the experience of joy, for it is already there inside. It is not merely that joy is within you, but that joy IS you! If you do not experience it all the time, then you are suffering from a case of mistaken identity, just like the lion cub that got separated from its mother.

Adopted by a sheep, the cub was raised by the flock in the wild, and learned to eat grass and to "baa." One day, drinking from a still pond, the now grown cub saw the reflection of another face staring back at him. The visitor's face was surprisingly familiar, with a golden mane like his own. The visitor asked him why he was eating grass and making such a disgraceful wimpy sound. "Why, because I am a sheep!" replied the cub. It took the visitor quite some time to convince the cub, "No, you are a lion. See, you look just like me." Eventually the cub realized his true nature and joyfully returned to the forest with his new friend.

This story has been handed down through the ages to remind you that you are not whom you think you are, and that you can easily recognize your true nature. Please take this reminder personally — your true nature is joy! This means you don't have to wait for everything in your life to be perfect in order to feel this joy. It is just beneath the part of yourself that you usually look at. It is there even when you do not have everything you want or when you're stuck with something you do not want. The joy of your own being is there even if your body is imperfect or your life needs some remodeling. To find it you merely need to stop trying so hard, because all the trying makes you think you can experience joy by adding something from the outside. When you succeed at adding some joy to your life, you have a temporary experience of "dependent joy." The problem with this is that it can only be created again by a lot of effort. Thus your life becomes constant hurrying from one temporary moment of dependent joy to another. This is not joy-fullness.

Yoga offers "independent joy." It arises from the core of your own being, like a geyser sprays a rising column of water into the air. You experience great joy when you watch jets of water shooting higher and higher, because you recognize that the experience of joy arises from within in this same way. Without depending on any specific external circumstances, you can (and must) find the inner wellspring of joy, which then fills you brimming to the top and overflows into your life. Instead of looking for joy to come from the events of your life, you can draw from your "joy-fullness" to express this joy in every action, in every relationship, in every thought and in every moment of every day.

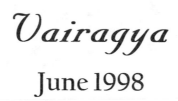

Vairagya

June 1998

"A full investigation into Truth will extinguish your desires at once, and the extinction will restore your mind to rest."

- Yoga Vasishtha

"Man is greater than all the objects of his desire."

- Rabindranath Tagore

This Sanskrit word is often translated as "non-attachment," but I prefer to think about it as "non-dependency." We have come to understand the trap of dependency quite well. Valuable techniques have been developed to help free us from our dependencies, including many twelve-step programs. A student told me (partly in jest) that she was considering joining the latest twelve-step program entitled, "Thinkers Anonymous." Yoga has been conducting Thinkers Anonymous programs for centuries!

One way to become free from your dependencies is through abstinence. However, you cannot totally abstain from some things like food, relationships, or thought. Instead, you must find how to nourish yourself well, enjoying the healthy pleasure provided by food, without falling into self-destructive food traps. You must learn how to use your mind without becoming trapped in your thoughts.

Yoga teaches you how to use your mind to think, and avoid using your thoughts to construct your sense of self. You discover how to eat well, without using food to fill you up, by finding the fullness of your own essence on the inside. You become active and effective in the world without using your activities to construct your identity. You enjoy relationships of all kinds without waiting for the others to make you feel loveable, because you are Love itself!

Yoga says you must know your True Self. Then you will be able to live your life fully, with a sense of freedom and joy. Any other way of living is like being in a portable prison of your own making. Do more yoga!

Abhyasa

July 1998

"That which we persist in doing becomes easier—not that the nature of the task has changed, but our ability to do it has increased."

- Ralph W. Emerson

"I know of no more encouraging fact than the unquestionable ability of man to elevate his life by conscious endeavor."

- Henry D. Thoreau

Perseverance is a key principle of yoga, as well as a skill that enhances the quality of your life. This Sanskrit word *abhyasa* means perseverance. It is also translated as vigilance. The vigilance is directed to yourself, noticing when you are slipping from your yogic State and then doing something to improve it immediately. A student recently described, "Now, whenever I do not feel happy, I know to do something about it immediately. I have a choice. I can change the way I feel, which then changes what I decide to do. Even stressful things aren't stressful any more. My whole life has opened up!"

To practice yoga in this way is a radical act. If you use the tools of yoga to monitor and fine tune your state (which includes your mood, emotions, attitude, mental state, and physical state), you will be radically different from everyone else, because you will be happy all the time. One of the curious side effects is that you will not have anything to talk about. Listen to the everyday conversations. Everyone is complaining about something. If you have nothing to complain about, what will you have to talk about? Try it for one day. It is a great yogic practice. For one full day, do not utter even a single complaint. You may find that you have very little to say!

The next stage of *abhyasa* is to maintain vigilance over your thoughts as well as your words. Do not allow your mind to peruse those old ruts any more. How do you stop? Simply use a yoga tool to divert your mind from its familiar routine. You can do a yoga pose — stand in *Tadasana*. Or sit quietly for a few long yoga breaths. Practice the yoga of the mind — remember a deep relaxation or meditation you have experienced, or bring to mind a contemplation from a recent class you have attended or book that you have read. Cultivate the yoga of the heart — expand your awareness to notice and to feel that you are surrounded and supported by the presence of the divine in this moment and in this place.

Yoga specializes in tricks and techniques to effect an immediate shift in your state. But none of them work unless you use them. A yoga teacher told me recently about some deep changes occurring in her body after several days of intense physical yoga practice. Never having experienced anything like this, she called a friend to come over and give her a massage. I asked her, "Why did not you do a soothing yoga pose or yoga breathing, to calm the effects and help along the changes?" She said, "I could not think of what to do. I forgot." If a teacher can forget, it is readily understandable that you might also lose track of what to do. This is why regular practice is so important. You must go to class or do your own practice regularly so that it becomes habit (a very beneficial habit); then you know what to do when you need it the most!

However, true *abhyasa* is noticing the slightest shift in your state and fine tuning it before it becomes a problem. It is like the small adjustments you make in your steering wheel as you drive down the road. Remain vigilant and notice when you are the slightest bit off. Persevere with the yoga practices when you need them *and* when you do not!

Choices

August 1998

"Choose always the way that seems best, however rought it may be; custom will soon render it easy and agreeable."

-Pythagoras

"Man is fully responsible for his nature and his choices."

-Jean-Paul Sartre

The two of them walked into the Danish bakery where I was standing, in Solvang, California. I watched as the father urged the nine-year-old to select a astry for his mother and aunt who were waiting in the car. The boy stared at his feet in terror that he might make the wrong choice. In the end, the father chose them himself. Then, the father said, "Okay. Just pick one for yourself." Immobilized, the boy could not choose. I said, "There is no wrong answer. Anything you choose is Okay." The boy looked up at me with tears in his eyes. Finally, his father made a selection for his son. They left.

We are always facing these kinds of choices. Every moment of every day, we are choosing what to eat, what to do next, whether to turn left or right at the next corner, who we speak to next, how we save or spend our money. The difficulty arises when we have the desire that our choice be the Right Choice, or the Best Choice. This Choice Must Make Me Happy!

But your practice of *vairagya* (nonattachment) and *abhyasa* (perseverance) create a difference. You reach the point where you no longer depend on the outer things for happiness. Now a choice becomes a simple choice. You can live with a tremendous sense of freedom, because you can choose anything (or nothing), and you are still completely happy. This is truly the free will that God meant for us to enjoy. Just choose!

Quiet Mind

September & October 1998

"Mind is only thoughts. The more easily you can be without thoughts, the nearer you are to a direct experience of Self."

-Lakshmana

"Conquer the mind, and you conquer the world."

-Guru Nanak

CR

A siren screams through the room where students are sitting motionless. A few are startled and turn their heads, though the ambulance is already gone. They turn back to an easy outer and inner stillness. Others, having cultivated their ability to sit in a yogic posture, remain outwardly still. After the class, some share that they did not even hear the ambulance, while others heard it and were undisturbed. Which of these is the yogic state of "Quiet Mind?"

Quiet Mind is an attainment as well as a practice. As an attainment, quiet mind is a steady state of non-distractibility. It is not the same as withdrawal or numbness. You hear the passing ambulance but are undisturbed, both inwardly and outwardly. In your daily life, caring involvement actually becomes more possible because you live in a consistent state of fearlessness and desirelessness. There is nothing to desire which could improve your inner state; there is nothing that must be avoided because it could diminish your inner state. Quiet mind is a portable yogic state that maximizes your enjoyment of life and your effectiveness in life.

Approached as a practice, quiet mind can take you to a deep meditative state called *samadhi*, where you do not even hear the outer sounds. It is a delicious feeling of inner absorption, from which you surface more fully refreshed than from sleep. It perpetually reinforces a deeper and more serene sense of Self.

When you are just beginning the practice of quiet mind, you may still hear and react to every sound; yet you return easily to quiet mind each time (this is called *abhyasa*, perseverance).

All of these are yogic states of Quiet Mind, which you can experience with some easy training. Your mind needs this training! You can use your body to develop quiet mind, by cultivating your ability to sit in an easy motionless posture. Your mind has been allowed to wander all over the cosmos for years. Now, you can treat your mind like a new puppy that you are training to walk on a leash. Do not jerk on the leash and yell at it, but call it lovingly back. Treat your mind lovingly, and it will love resting in its own inner source.

When I hear a siren, my personal practice is to include it in my perception while remaining inwardly (and outwardly) peaceful. I also offer blessings to all who are affected — those in need of the emergency assistance, their family and friends, and those who provide the help. In this small way, I can participate rather than withdraw, even as I sit in quiet mind.

Gratitude

November & December 1998

*"When you drink from the stream,
remember the source."*

- Chinese Proverb

*"Reflect upon your present blessings, of which every man has many;
not on your misfortunes, of which all men have some."*

- Charles Dickens

You can celebrate Thanksgiving Day without feeling thankful. It can even become a celebration of greed instead of gratitude. Before you can feel gratitude, you have to see for what there is to be grateful. Finding the blessings in your life is dependent on what you look at, not on how well your life is going. This shows up even in yoga class.

I enjoy helping new students settle in for their first guided relaxation. They lay down on the floor. I bring cushions and blankets and then I adjust them to make them more comfortable. I begin with one shoulder, sliding the shoulder blade down their back gently, to lay it flatter on the floor. Perhaps you already know how good this feels. Then I stop and ask, "How does your right shoulder feel compared to your left?" The range of answers is amazing!

Many students close their eyes and sigh, "It feels flatter, softer and more relaxed." Others open their eyes wide and begin looking around, as though they might find the answer written on the ceiling. Finally they say, "It feels better." Not sure if their answer is right, they put a question mark on it. I ask again, "Better... in what way?" They cast around again, their difficulty arising from the fact that this is an entirely new feeling for them. Finally, they state quite definitively, "It feels more relaxed." Some will say it feels lighter or heavier, or both. Others describe it as "more energy flowing through." Others say it is wide, or lower, or "fluffier." Anything they say is correct, because they are reporting their own experience.

But some tell me, "My left shoulder feels tighter." They don't notice the improvements. Instead, they focus on the discomfort in the other shoulder. Some go on to describe ten years of history with shoulder problems, not noticing that something has changed. If I point out, "I moved your right shoulder," they say, "You did?" They have a tendency to always focus on the problem, or on their history of past problems. This is a problem in itself. It's like seeing the world in black and white instead of color; or it is like monovision where you have no depth perception. Everything seems flat and colorless. They have no joy, no gratitude.

This changes, of course, with regular yoga practice. Along with becoming more flexible and less stressed, you begin to see your life differently. You see the color and the depth in every moment. When one shoulder is tight and one is relaxed, you can notice the relaxed one. You even laugh at the difference between them. You begin to see the light in your life instead of obsessing on the dark spots. Your perception changes. You see your life and yourself differently. Then you can experience gratitude. You begin to live with an attitude of gratitude. Life is good.

Bliss

December 1998

"*If you follow your bliss, doors will open for you
that wouldn't have opened for anyone else.*"

- Joseph Campbell

"*Realize the essence of your own being and you will never again get lost
in the world, the home of all sorrows. You will love your life in freedom
and biss of the knowing of your own essence.*"

- Rama Berch as inspired by *Viveka-Chudamani*

What is bliss? People sometimes ask me this question, which I find difficult to answer. It is like trying to describe the taste of chocolate-covered strawberries to someone who has never tasted chocolate or strawberries. Words are inadequate. Only the experience counts.

You have experienced bliss before, though you may not have known what to call it. Everyone has his or her favorite ways of triggering the bliss experience, because it is an essential part of life. Without bliss, you begin to feel that life has no meaning. Bliss is an essential part of life because it is your own essence. If you don't connect with your own essence frequently enough, you may question the value of life itself.

The Holiday Season is a time we are all ready for bliss. Some people find it by overeating. If you *really* overdo it, like at Thanksgiving dinner, it is not at all blissful. But if you just eat your fill (and maybe a bit more), there is this wonderful feeling of satiation that is a type of bliss. This type of bliss is *tamasic*, meaning heavy and inert. Other types of *tamasic* bliss include the use of drugs, alcohol and television.

Rajasic bliss is the type you get from vigorous exercise or through emotionalism or confrontation. Workaholics are addicted to *rajasic* bliss, which comes from a feeling of accomplishment mixed with exhaustion. Many people cannot even sleep until they have exhausted themselves. They may have to stay up very late in order to find this.

Svaroopa Yoga provides *sattvic* bliss, which is imbued with the qualities of clarity and openness. It is the feeling you have after you come up from your final *Shavasana* (relaxation pose), both relaxed and alert. Most people associate relaxed with couch-potatoness (*tamasic*). They associate alert with being on edge (*rajasic*). Relaxed and alert is a new combination. Yoga gives you a whole new type of bliss to experience. It also provides you with tools to reconnect with it often — through a breath or a stretch, or by doing some yoga at home or in a class. More yoga — more bliss.

Change & the Changeless

January 1999

*"You are not here to change the world.
The world is here to change you."*

- Shantidasa

*"There are no quick fixes that can
permanently change your life."*

- Sonya Friedman

Whatever happened to New Year's resolutions? Everyone tells me, "Oh, I do not make them any more." Why not? Are you so perfect that there is nothing you need to change? It is important to have a point in time, so you can make an appraisal of how you are doing. It is even more important to resolve to improve, *and then act upon that resolve.*

Change comes in many forms. You can choose it, or it can be forced on you. When your employer "reorganizes" your job out of existence or your spouse decides upon a new lifestyle, you undergo a lot of change. Simpler changes are imposed on you all the time, like when your favorite brand is no longer available, or they rewrote the weekly television schedule. Perhaps your yoga teacher switches class to a different day and time. These externals compel a change, whether you wanted it or not. When students tell me about the experiences that helped them become who they are now, they usually talk about something they resisted when it first arose. Change is inevitable, and it impels you into needed personal growth.

Change can also be created through your own choice. You can be the employee or spouse leaving the relationship. You can decide to change your eating habits or to become more regular in your yoga practice. The choice to change comes from two types of motivations: novelty and commitment. Some people keep their life interesting by constant change. Life is boring without something new and interesting. I know this one well because I spent twenty years practicing it before I found yoga. In fact, yoga was one of the things I tried in my endless search for something new and satisfying. Yoga surprised me by becoming progressively more satisfying. It ended my dependency on the "new and improved" activities to animate my life.

New Year's resolutions are about choosing to change through clarity and commitment: to see yourself in a moment of clarity, and to commit to give birth to the changes in yourself that you choose. To give up on making resolutions is like giving up on yourself. To give up on making resolutions is to choose that changes will be forced upon you, because life will not let you resign from the process of growth and transformation. In fact, each of the steps in your process of personal growth brings you closer to the experience of what yoga calls the Changeless. This is the essence of your being, which creates the continuity of the sense of "I" throughout all the changes. But, we'll discuss more about that later . . .

What are your resolutions for the New Year? What will you choose to change?

☙

The Changeless

February 1999

*"All changes are taking place in the universe as willed by the divine.
Changes are due to the very fact that this manifestation
is not permanent. It is ever-changing.
But the Spirit underlying the universe is eternal and changeless."*

-Papa Ramdas

*"Know that it is the image that changes;
the true Self never moves or changes."*

- Vachaka Kovia

In all the changes of life, one thing remains changeless. It is an inner continu-ity which yoga calls the Self. Even when everything changes on the outside, you are still "you." Even when everything changes on the inside, the "you" that you are is the same "you" as when you were a child. Your body has changed in many ways, but you are still "you." This is the Changeless Self.

This Changeless Self inside you is inside everyone. People are very different on the outside, but there is one Self in all. We recognize this essence in another when we look deeply into their eyes. We see something that makes us value each human life, regardless of who they are, or how or where they live.

Yoga is the Science of Consciousness. It offers teachings and practices that have a predictable effect — you find that Changeless Self. When you find the unchanging essence inside, you are peaceful, even in the midst of chaos. You feel full inside and completely supported, even in the face of crisis or loss. You are compassionate, even to those who have harmed others (or yourself). This happens because you do not depend on the externals to construct your sense of self. You have an independent source inside. You live in a constant stream of inner nourishment.

Without it, you feel lost. When you feel lost, everything you do in life is to (hopefully) stimulate the experience of your Changeless Self. Every activity, every relationship and all the changes you undergo are attempts to get that moment of supreme satisfaction, like hitting the home run that wins the game. If you are too distant from your Changeless Self, you may begin to think that life has no meaning. Yet, the meaning is inside you all the while. Look inside.

Wisdom

March 1999

"Mere silence is not wisdom, for wisdom consists in knowing when
and how to speak and when and where to keep silent."

- Jean Pierre Camus

"Many men can utter words of wisdom,
few men can practice it themselves."

- Hitopadesa

A mother brought her twelve-year-old daughter in with back pain. I spent some time with them both. As they left, the mother remarked, "You are really good with kids." I responded that I raised three of my own. She replied, "Yes, but that would not necessarily mean you would be good with them." In that moment, I realized that it takes experience and understanding together to make Wisdom.

One who has experience in dealing with children, but has no understanding of them, lacks wisdom in regard to children. Experience alone is not enough. Likewise, those who have understanding without experience cannot be called wise. A student described to me that she became a licensed psychologist in her twenties. She listened as those with decades of life experience poured out their fears and needs. She was thinking, "I have never experienced this. How can I really help?" I am sure she did help, just by listening. But the theories she had learned weren't enough for her to feel wise. Understanding alone is not enough.

In yoga, we cultivate understanding and experience simultaneously. In class, the teachers often ask you to notice the differences in your body after a pose, and even to describe them. By putting words to your experience, you develop your understanding. The teachers may say things like, "This is good for your spine. Can you feel it lengthening?" Then you go looking for it in your own body, and you are putting understanding and experience together.

The fullest expression of Wisdom is the simultaneous experience and understanding of Consciousness. The Wise One lives in the knowing and experience of, "I am the Self; divine Consciousness is my essence." The teachings of yoga come from countless generations of such Masters, to help us know that this is inside each of us. The practices help us find the experience inside. This combination of understanding and experience is True Wisdom. It is your destiny!

Action & Motivation

April 1999

"The difference between what we do and what we are capable of doing would suffice to solve most of the world's problems."

- Mohandas Gandhi

"Heaven never helps the man who will not act."

- Sophocles

Wisdom without action is delusion. Wisdom is the combination of experience and understanding together, so there must be action to acquire wisdom. You cannot have experience without engaging in action. Yet action does not end with merely acquiring a large number of experiences. One who becomes truly wise continues to perform actions, but with different motivations. Then all actions (and all of life itself) become a living yoga practice that leads to wisdom. You get there by examining your motivations.

There are three primary motivations underlying most people's actions: protection, relationship, and recognition. Each is actually an attempt to construct a sense of personal identity. But any sense of personal identity that you are able to *construct* will not last, because it is *constructed* rather than being inherent. The practices of yoga help you discover the underlying sense of self that has always been there. It currently supports you (behind your mind). It will never cease to exist. Your discovery of this deeper dimension of your own being is the most satisfying experience of your life. However, the constructed identity is a superficial sense of self and is dependent on your own effort to create and maintain it.

For example, you may decide to improve your performance at work. This decision could arise from one of many different reasons: so that you can keep your job when the layoffs come (protection), because your boss is trusting and relying upon you (relationship), or to gain a raise or promotion (recognition). These are called self-motivated actions, because they are motivated by the desire to construct a superficial sense of self. Self-motivated actions bring *karmic* backlash. Plus, they are never fully effective.

The practices of yoga provide you with increasingly powerful tastes of your own essence, which make you more and more free from the need to construct a superficial identity. The old motivations dissolve away, until action seems no longer necessary. However, if those with wisdom ceased all activity, the world would be taken over by fools. More importantly, true wisdom always brings compassion along with it, so the wise ones continue to serve others through action. These actions have no ulterior motives hidden within them and are fully effective in the world.

If you examine your motivations, you can turn all your actions into a living yoga practice that leads you to true wisdom. Observe yourself for the next few minutes. See why it is that you do what you do. You may be able to engage in the same activity you had planned, but in a different way — without the motive of constructing a superficial identity. This yoga practice can give you an immediate sense of great freedom, accompanied by a joyful boundlessness of being. This can be extended indefinitely by merely continuing this simple practice of examining your motives for action. If you forget this practice and get caught up in the self-motivated actions again, a yoga class will make all the difference in the world, and make it easier for you to return to yoga's path of action. Do more yoga.

Ego

May 1999

"*The ego is a self-satisfying historian which seeks only that information that agrees with it, rewrites history when it needs to, and does not even see the evidence that threatens it.*"

- Anthony G. Greenwald

"*The best way of seeing divine light is to put out your own little candle.*"

- English Proverb

Your mind's job is to doubt (and it's doing a very good job). It distrusts everything and everyone, keeping you in a state of unrelenting anxiety and a feeling of distance from others. Yoga calls this part of your mind *ahamkara*, which is usually translated as "ego." This is different from what most people mean by the word "ego," thinking of someone as having a big ego when they act in certain ways. Yoga says that such a person has a small ego, because they have to act this way to counteract the way they really feel inside. *Ahamkara* is a specific aspect of your mind that makes you feel small and inadequate. It has a million ways of chopping you down to size. It even has the effect of shrinking or compressing your body. You actually get shorter when you feel yourself to be small. By doing yoga poses, you begin reversing this process by elongating your spine. This naturally expands your sense of self, propelling you beyond *ahamkara* into *svaroopa*, the Bliss of your own Being.

Ahamkara is the part of your mind that acts like a barbed wire fence, carving a specific territory out of Consciousness-Itself to name as your own, and then doubting everything else. You live inside this small section that is your own personal turf instead of recognizing the vastness of your true identity. *Ahamkara* specializes in reminding you of how small and inadequate you are, constantly reinforcing your seeming separation from Consciousness-Itself. "Do not degrade yourself," says Krishna in the <u>Bhagavadgita</u>, an important yoga text. This is a powerful reminder and important yoga practice that is actually more important than the yoga poses. Think well of yourself!

The average person thinks 65,000 thoughts per day. The problem is that this is not a constant stream of new, creative, uplifting and inspiring thoughts. Not only are they repetitive, too many of them are demeaning. If you spoke to your friends this way, you would not have any friends. It does not matter when you learned to talk to yourself this way or from whom you learned it. It is time to make a change.

When you notice that your mind is on automatic pilot, you must intervene. Do not merely watch your mind — do something different with it! Take a long in-breath with an especially slow exhale. Do a yoga pose or indulge in a nice stretch. Replace that thought by thinking something positive about yourself or you may find it easier to think something positive about someone else. Perhaps you need a mantra that you can repeat silently inside, to replace all those unnecessary thoughts that continually re-construct the barbed wire fences of your *ahamkara*. You must retrain your mind so that it no longer limits your sense of self, but becomes a window through which you can look inward to the inner vastness of your own being.

Sense of Purpose

June 1999

"Purpose is what gives life meaning."

— Charles Parkhurst

*"Who stands already on heaven's topmost dome
needs not to search for ladders."*

— Rumi

"Ego is the bad stuff," one student said authoritatively. "Yes," I replied, "*and ego is the good stuff, too!*" For example, if you quit smoking, you can feel quite virtuous, and even become quite obnoxious to others about your reformed ways. Your old identity as a smoker has been replaced by a new sense of identity as a non-smoker — but it is still a way of saying, "I am what I do." Your mind performs this insidious function called *ahamkara*, which means "I am what I do." *Ahamkara* is usually translated as "ego," which is misleading because we think of ego as being the bad stuff.

Ego makes you think that you are not a divine incarnation of perfect consciousness, at play in a world of consciousness. Ego makes you *not* live in the knowing of the Bliss Of Your Own Being. It is an inner separation from your true Self that turns into the inner dialogues. It creates the drama of your life played out in never-ending thoughts. Ego makes you feel not good enough, not strong enough, not pretty enough, and not thin enough (even when you are). It makes you try harder, go faster, and do more. Ego is the voice that whines, "Why am I here, anyway?"

It is ego that feels incomplete and yearns for a sense of purpose in life. *USA Today* reported that one third of Americans would ask God, "What is my purpose in life?" That is a lot of people! Fortunately, many of them come to yoga classes. When you look around the yoga classroom, remember that there are many there who share your same yearning. This sense of purpose is called *dharma*, and is the "why" you are here and the "what" you are supposed to be doing.

The *Isha Upanishad* says that it is your *dharma* to know the true Self, which is Consciousness-Itself being you. Without this attainment, you will always be striving for something. You can attain all the awards, know all the right people, vacation in all the places on your list, and you will *still* be adding more things to that wish list. This is because of ego — *ahamkara* always feels incomplete. *Ahamkara* says, "I am not the whole of Consciousness. I am less. Therefore, I need something to complete me. What is that perfect something that will make me feel complete?" So, the search begins. And it goes on, and on, and on . . .

The purpose of your life is to know the true Self. The things you love to do the most are the things that give you momentary flashes of the Bliss of Your Own Being. You have had this experience when you watched a sunset or climbed to the top of the mountain, or when you looked deep into someone's eyes and truly connected, or just when you heard your cat purr. But these are only momentary flashes. Then ego forces you to move on. Ego says, "I am what I do. Even though this thing took me to the Bliss Of My Own Being, I must keep doing. So, what is next?"

How do you get out of this trap? Do more yoga! Yoga gives you a direct route to the experience of the true Self, while it develops your ability to stay in it progressively longer. Then you will not ask for the people and things in your life to make you feel whole. You take the inner fullness and pour it into your life. In this way, you can keep the same job, live in the same house, drive the same car, stay with the same spouse, and feel that you are expressing your purpose in life. Because your life becomes the expression of your true Self. Anything less than this will not be enough.

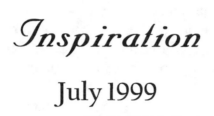

Inspiration

July 1999

"Do not quench your inspiration and your imagination;
do not become the slave of your model."

— Vincent Van Gogh

It cannot be denied. When the inner prompting arises — the song must be sung, the painting painted, and the newfound clarity spoken aloud. You have these moments, when everything shines brightly and the colors of the flowers (and even the passing cars) are crisp and clear. There are, of course, the other kinds of days. Artists and musicians despair when the flow dries up. Writers go to workshops on "Getting Past Writer's Block." You live in quiet despair, wondering what life is all about, or filling up your days with endless activity to entertain the mind (translate — to distract you from your misery).

Inspiration is the outpouring of the Self from within, and you love it! Life makes sense. You fathom the "more" than what life seems to be on the surface. What if you didn't have to wait for the mercurial muse — if you could tap into the flow of creativity or establish mental clarity any time you wanted? When would you choose to be out of that flow? You think that inspiration is tempo-rary and fragile. Yoga says that it is your Self. Your connection with that is tenuous. It can be strengthened through practice. Practice means that you establish the inner connection again and again. You practice until you get good at being Self, which is Consciousness-Itself. Then you live from the inner wellspring of Being, and every word and every action is inspired. Do not settle for less!

Inspiration is not the same as imagination. Imagination is an activity of mind, which can be a creative delight or something much less positive. Most people use their imagination to construct an endless stream of worries (imagining all the bad things that can happen), or to fantasize about the future (imagining what you would do with your lottery winnings), or to think about all the bad things people are saying about you (this form of imagination is called para-noia), etc. You can even create paintings, music and poetry from your mind. But the most moving creations are the ones that come from beyond the mind. There must be an inner surrender, so the inner prompting may arise and command your mind.

What if you could speak to that inner source and ask it to fill you? What would you call it? Yoga calls it "Saraswati," the Goddess of Wisdom and Learning, the Fount of Creativity, the "Patron Saint" of poets, scholars, artists and musicians. She is the energy that arises within you as that flow of inspiration, lifting you to new levels of your own potential. By giving this energy a name, you are able to ask for Her blessings and support. The traditional *puja* ceremony is a way to we invoke Her presence in a tangible and powerful way. As a teaching institution, every class we offer is an expression of her generosity and blessings.

Yoga practices clear away the blocks that impede your experience of inspiration, Saraswati's blessing. Whether you lie in *Shavasana* for a relaxation, take a few slow *Ujjayi* breaths, or do some yoga poses, you feel different afterward. Meditation dissolves the blocks even more powerfully, as does *karma yoga* (offering your service to others). Many students find they become more creative when they practice yoga on a regular basis. May Saraswati's blessings inspire you to greater experiences and deeper understandings.

Grace

August 1999

"The breeze of grace is always blowing on you.
You have to open the sails and your boat will move forward."

— Ramakrishna

"The way of grace is mysterious.
You struggle for it and you do not get it.
Sometimes, without any struggle, you get it.
Its working is governed by something beyond all laws.
It is not bound by any rules, regulations or conditions."

— Papa Ramdas

Grace is one of the primary principles of yoga. Grace makes things easy. It is always flowing. If life seems hard to you, you have unknowingly shut yourself off from the flow of grace. Yoga opens you up to its support in many tangible ways.

The principle of support is a primary element of *Svaroopa Yoga* practice. Your teacher may slide a blanket underneath you in a seated position in order for you to get the most benefit. Halfway through the pose, she may remind you, "Lean your full weight into the support of that blanket." Most people do not really sit on the blanket or chair underneath them, but hold themselves up by tightening their spinal muscles. Check in with yourself right now. Are you leaning your full weight into the support underneath you? As you lean more fully into your seat, you may find that you significantly relax and can breathe more easily. Learning to lean into the physical support is a way of practicing how to lean into the support of grace.

Let down your walls. They not only isolate you from others — they separate you from the flow of grace. Learning how to relax in *Shavasana* is learning how to melt the walls. The progressive release of *Shavasana* becomes deeper and more reliable with repetition. When you have been doing *Shavasana* at the beginning and end of each yoga class for another year, you will slip more easily and more deeply inside than you do now. This also provides you with a deeper sense of personal center, which psychologists call "an inner locus of control." You can go into the world and into your relationships without those old walls any more, and you can experience the ever-present flow of grace much more tangibly.

Every football team has a "Receiver." His job is to place himself in the right spot on the playing field and wait for the ball. Yoga helps you position yourself in the playing field of life so that you become a Receiver of grace. It makes your mind clearer, so you can see your options. The actions you undertake become easier to do and more effective. Grace is like the moving sidewalk at the airport; each step you make takes you a little further.

Your own self-effort is an important part of grace. Keep moving in any direction, even if it's the wrong one. It is easier for grace to steer you in the right direction than to push you from a dead stop. Even the winners of the lottery have to buy the ticket. In the same way, sometimes the hardest part of yoga is just getting to the class. This makes your yoga class a perfect combination of self-effort and grace. Now all you have to do is learn to live your life this way.

Teaching

September 1999

"To teach is to learn twice."

— Joseph Joubert

"Learning is not the accumulation of knowledge.
Learning is movement from moment to moment."

— J. Krishnamurti

I remember being asked repeatedly, "What do you want to be when you grow up?" I could never have imagined I would be a yoga teacher (and probably neither could my high school guidance counselor). The die was cast early for me: I began teaching when I was in fifth grade. My teacher let me leave class every day to go assist the kindergarten teacher. Even through the years in the business world, I was always training staff and clients. But teaching yoga is the best!

Teaching puts the yoga teacher in the flow of grace in a way that merely doing personal practice can never open up. You may have already noticed that being a student in a yoga class provides you with more benefits than doing your practice at home. The group energy and focus definitely play a part in this, but that is not all. There is something more. Grace flows through the generations of teachers, stretching back to the beginning of yoga, which was at the beginning of human existence. The teacher and everyone in class are bathed in this flow. The teacher experiences it as flowing through him or her, like a river coursing through his or her essence and being. A teacher is at her best when she is having this inner experience while talking and moving through the class — and the students know the difference!

I remember when a Teacher Training graduate returned from teaching one of her first solo classes. She was excited and amazed to report that she had leaned all the way forward into a deep angle for the first time ever during this class. She tipped forward to show me — but could not go as far as she had during the class. Shock registered on her face, for she had done the full pose just an hour before! This flow of grace is one of the best-kept secrets of yoga — and it is one of the reasons yoga teachers love to teach so much.

I am constantly re-inspired by the love and dedication with which *Svaroopa*-style teachers serve their students. While they serve others, they get to live in the flow of grace that supports and reveals ever more and more. You can, too. Do more yoga.

Breathing

October 1999

"He lives most life whoever breathes most air."
— Elizabeth Barrett Browning

"As for the proper inner breath, it is called the Embryonic breath.
Since it is naturally inside you, you do not have to seek outside for it."
— Master Great Nothing of Sung-Shan

Check and see right now — are you breathing? Take a breath — and let it out slow and long. If your exhale is truly slow AND long, your next inhale will be easy and full. Your exhalation is the key to your breath. Do it again — a long slow exhale. How does it feel?

"Waiting to Exhale" was a great movie title because it named a reality. You are always waiting to exhale. You are always holding your breath. You have heard the phrase, "Do not hold your breath." It means that the thing you are waiting for is not coming to you imminently. You are always holding your breath because you are always waiting for something — something that will make it okay for you to breathe. Consider, what one "thing" could possibly happen in your life that would make it okay for you to breathe easy? The reality is that no one "thing" will do it for you. Even if you do get all the "things" in place, they are likely to shift around again. Then, you are back to waiting. So, you need to breathe anyway. Just exhale. Give a long slow sigh of relief and the things won't seem so important. But even more than giving yourself an occasional long breath, your whole breathing style needs to change.

The average eighty-year-old person breathes one half of the amount of the average thirty-year-old. Imagine if you breathed only one half of the amount you currently breathe. Unfortunately, knowing about this is not enough. It is impossible to remember to breathe more — breathing happens spontaneously (thank heaven!). You need to do something that reprograms your everyday breath, so that each breath is naturally easier and more open.

Every yoga class begins with the full yoga breath, *Ujjayi Pranayama*. It is incredibly beneficial if you incorporate it into your daily life. The easiest way is to do it in bed before you go to sleep at night. Your sleep will be deeper and more restful. You may even need less sleep!

The five elements of *Ujjayi Pranayama*, in order of their importance, are:

1. making the breathing sound in your throat (on both the exhalation and inhalation),
2. slowing down and smoothing out the pace of the breaths (which makes the breathing sound quieter),

3. gently extending the length of each inhalation and each exhalation,
4. increasing the quantity of breath that you fill in and empty out *without straining or forcing,*
5. sequencing or placing the breath in specific interior spaces.

Developing these qualities makes *Ujjayi Pranayama* a profound and powerful practice. It can cure allergies and free you from all anxieties. It will create vibrant health and vitality as well as lay the foundation for you to experience deep meditation.

Ujjayi Pranayama is not the way you are supposed to breathe all the time. It is impossible to remember to breathe this way all day long. You are not supposed to have to remember to breathe. Do it only ten- or twenty-minutes per day. Within a few days, you will find that your usual breathing style has changed without you having to pay any attention to it. You will no longer be waiting to exhale, because you will no longer be holding your breath or waiting for some "thing" to happen. Life will be rich and satisfying just the way it is.

Motivation

November 1999

"Every good work we do without any ulterior motive, instead of forging a new chain, will break one of the links in the existing chains. Every good thought that we send to the world without thinking of any return will be stored up there, and break one link in the chain, and make us purer and purer, until we become the purest of mortals."

— Swami Vivekananda

"If you can welcome somebody without any selfish motive, then you experience the joy of the Self in your own heart."

— Swami Chidvilasananda

Why you do *what* you do is more important than *how* you do it. This is because why you do something affects what you choose to do, as well as how you actually do it. Every single goal can be traced to one source — a desire to feel happy. Everything you want to accomplish, everywhere you go, and everyone you choose to spend time with is for one purpose — to make you feel happy. Some of you may be objecting, "I do not go to work so that I will feel happy. I feel happy when I leave work!" You may not love your job, but you do go to work in order to have a place to live, pay your bills, and buy necessities as well as luxuries. The alternative would not feel happy at all. In fact, a job is considered to be a good one when you actually like doing it (or doing most of the parts of it) — which is again about feeling happy.

A student recently described her beautiful vacation in Ireland. She had a wonderful time and learned a lot, not just about Ireland, but also about herself. I know others who have spent their vacation time doing hard physical labor on charitable projects, returning home feeling really happy. Both of these are good things, chosen so that they would feel happy.

There is an underlying problem — you do not already feel happy. You have to do only certain things and not do others in order to feel happy. If you do not, you will not feel happy. The goal of yoga is to change it all, by discovering the inner source of happiness. The way you feel after a yoga class or after you do yoga is an immediate taste of this independent happiness. When you feel this way, there is no need for doing a particular thing, and no aversion to doing it — the usual motivation is gone. Now your array of choices becomes limitless. You can choose to do or to not do any thing, go or not go to any place, see or not see any person, but the *why* has changed. There is no need that the activity pays off with a certain outcome, because the way you would have felt after its completion is already full and complete within you. You are actually no longer motivated at all, but you can participate in everything with great happiness.

Motivation is one of the themes painted clearly in the *Mahabharata*, an ancient Indian epic. The main protagonist vehemently exclaims, "I *want* to be discontented!" A wealthy and powerful King for twenty years or more, he has everything he desires including power, wealth, the love and support of his family, and respect of other kings. He has everything except the one thing he wants above

126

all else, the destruction of his royal cousins, who are ethically and spiritually his betters. If he allows himself to be happy with his life as it is, he would have to give up his passion to destroy his cousins. He clings fiercely to his self-destructive unhappiness, which drives him relentlessly. It ultimately brings about world war. This world war caused the death of millions, annihilating the race of great warriors at the end of the Third Great Age, around five thousand years ago.

The lessons in this history are as alive and meaningful today, as we draw close to the ending of this millennium. They offer us an opportunity to see ourselves in the light of Ancient Truths. The _Mahabharata_ story offers you a way to look at your own life. May yoga give you new eyes to see it all clearly.

Light

December 1999

"Light and darkness cannot exist at the same time.
When you bring in light, darkness must fly;
no matter what darkness it is, it must fly. So that is the power of light."

-Chidananda

"Give light and the darkness will disappear on itself."

-Erasmus

＄

It seems strange that we celebrate light at the darkest time of year — when we have the shortest days and longest nights. As we pass the winter solstice and celebrate such meaningful holidays, we continue the ancient ritual of lighting outside and inside our homes. The earth turns on its axis to begin bringing us longer days and our calendar turns on its heel, facing us squarely into the mirror so we can see ourselves! Can we find the light within?

One part of the ancient epic *Mahabharata* brings us to a scene where we find a great hero, Arjuna, suffering darkness and despair. Through a series of foul deeds, his beloved son has been killed in battle. Now Arjuna suffers. He is in danger of losing his clarity about why he must fight this war. Earlier, Krishna led him through confusion into clarity. Arjuna had been fighting skillfully, while never losing sight of the higher purpose he is serving in the midst of the chaos. Now grief moves him dangerously close to acting out of anger and desire for revenge.

Krishna says to him, "I am crossing the great era of darkness with you. This struggle is absolute; you and your brothers are the world's only light. If your heart breaks or closes up, if it becomes bitter, dark or dry, the light will be lost." No matter what, you must keep your heart open. The light is found in the center of your heart, and it shines through your eyes. Your heart must remain open, or everything is lost!

The holidays should be the time where this is easiest, but the reality is often very different. Holiday stress is not an oxymoron anymore. You may have emotional residue from Christmas Past, which stays safely hidden during the rest of the year. Perhaps the reality of your family just does not meet the expectations of the idea of which you still dream. Maybe the list of things that must be done is beyond the capacity of any superhero. So you begin to close up.

What is the answer? More yoga! The fanatic in me loves being able to repeat this again. Ask yourself, "What really does work for me?" Will another eggnog or glass of champagne do it? "If your heart breaks or closes up, if it becomes bitter, dark or dry, the light will be lost." You must keep your heart open. You must shine your light into the world. Yoga gives you the tools; all you have to do is use them.

The light that must be found is inside your Self. You do not merely find that light within — you *are* that light. Finding it is not just a survival tool for the holidays, it is a life skill that will be needed in the New Year and every day. You are nothing without that light. You can travel all over the world, select the perfect gifts for all the people on your lists, and bake the perfect pie, but it will all be meaningless if you do not find the inner light that is your essence and being. You must know your Self!

The Future is Now!

January 2000

"Do not blame Karma or anybody else, for what you are.
You can undo what has been done,
through the exercise of a determined will."

- Papa Ramdas

January 1st of any year is no different than other day, except that we agree on a special name for it, "New Year's Day." The universe did not begin 2000 years ago, so it is really not a "new" year or a "new" millennium. Even the names we give to the days of the week have no real significance. However, more people die of heart attacks on Monday mornings between 3 and 7 a.m. than any other day and time. Doctors tell us that squirrels die of heart attacks too, but no more of them die on Monday mornings than on other days. That is because squirrels don't have Mondays. We are affected because we layer meanings onto the names of the days and the activities related to them. They are very real for us — and can even be fatal.

The New Year and New Millennium are created by the mind, but the mind is incredibly powerful! Your mind creates your reality. You perceive things around you, make decisions and then carry them into action, which affects you and the world around you. This is the law of *karma* — what you do has an effect, what you say has an even stronger effect, and what you *think* has the strongest effect of all. So — what do you *think* of the New Millennium? Is this all hype, or is it that once-in-a-lifetime opportunity? What you think determines what you will do with it.

The *Shiva Sutras* describe the state of an enlightened being: *iccha shaktir uma-kumari* — s/he lives in the fullness of knowing of every moment as a divine moment, blossoming with the newness of spring and saturated with the joy of a newborn baby. For such a master, every moment is a golden one. There is no need for an annual rite of new beginnings. But, the rest of us need a jump-start.

You lay the seeds of your own future in what you think and in what you decide to do. If you go to yoga classes, you will feel better and be healthier. If you do not do yoga, how will you feel in another two years? You may have already proved to yourself that your body needs some help.

Yoga offers more than physical benefits. It is not merely about *how* you feel. It is really about *who* you feel yourself to be. With regular yoga practice, your sense of self is based in a deeper inner dimension of reality and is less a function of the outer world. In other words, you develop an inner locus of control — you are less a victim of circumstances. You may even find some of that "inner bliss" that everyone is talking about!

When you take yoga classes, you will also improve other people's lives. One man came to his wife's graduation from our Teacher Training program and announced that he had recommended that everyone in his office do yoga. We asked, "Why? You are not doing it yourself." He said, "Yes, but my life has improved so much since my wife began yoga, I figured it would get even better if everyone at work would do it." Smart man. Now, he is even smarter — he is doing yoga himself!

Your future arises from the present. What you are doing right now determines how you will feel later today, as well as tomorrow and the rest of your life. The New Millennium is a golden opportunity — what are you doing with it? Allow it to jump-start you and get you into gear. Do more yoga!

Path with a Heart

February 2000

"The spirit of life ... dwells in the secret chamber of the heart."
                                                              - Dante Alighieri

""The heart sometimes finds out things that reason cannot."
                                                              - Louis de Montfort

Your mind is not capable of love. Your mind is a limited tool. It is not able to experience love or happiness. For you to be able to feel the feeling of love, your mind must get out of the way. When you feel happy, truly happy, your mind is completely still. Both love and happiness arise from a deeper level of your being. They stream up, through and past your mind.

Likewise, your mind cannot hold Consciousness. Your mind is a creation of Consciousness, which creates all things, but is a limited form of Consciousness. Your mind can conceive of the existence of Consciousness, which yoga calls "Self", but cannot know it. Your mind must surrender to Self. Yet, in yoga you work with your mind, just as you must work with your body. You must retrain your mind and clear out the things that limit your ability to experience the Self.

As a teacher, I was trained in these principles. I even memorized the *sutras* (*Sanskrit* aphorisms), but did not really understand them. Without realizing it, I still approached yoga as though I could know Consciousness with my mind. I felt that I would eventually "get it." I would eventually be able to grasp it with my intellect and know it with my mind. Then I met a *Guru* who had done it that way. What a wonderful lesson!

I went to a *satsang* (gathering of seekers) where people could ask questions of this *Guru*. While I sat with everyone else, waiting for him to come into the room, I read the printed page describing his background. It described how he was thrust into a moment of clarity by watching a bird fly across the sky. He seized that moment then, and continues to live in it now.

When he entered the room and sat with us, I was surprised to see that he continually squinted his eyes and peered into space, as though he was focusing on some distant object. Occasionally, he would look at a person who raised their hand to ask a question, and then look back into the distance. He paused after hearing the question as though he was straining to hear some distant sound. He seemed to me that he was always reaching or straining for some-thing that was almost unreachable.

I became increasingly uncomfortable as I listened to the questions and his answers, finally wiggling and shifting in my chair constantly. To me, his answers were dry and so intellectual that I could not relate to them. Yet he truly spoke with a tremendous clarity and insight. It just seemed like it was coming from a book — to me, it was not alive. After ten- or fifteen-minutes, I left. I knew it was disrespectful, but I could not stay!

I went home and sat in my living room, contemplating what I had experienced. Then, I saw that he had given a gift to me. I saw the opportunity to step into the clarity he lived in, just as one would open a sliding glass door and step through. I knew that, in that moment, I could become enlightened. I had a sense that I had stepped previously through that door, in the distant past, in another life. I hesitated. I was surprised that I did not seize this tremendous opportunity! I inquired further into myself, why was I waiting?

Then I saw that this path had no heart. This would be (for me) an experience of Consciousness but without love. And I knew in that moment that I didn't want that kind of enlightenment. Give me a path with heart, I prayed. Since then, I have enjoyed every encounter with every person so much more. I have been able to give up the desire to control others. Now I delight in the unexpected twists and turns of being in relationship. I know that every person I meet is another teacher who will help me to find enlightenment with heart. And I know that every moment of working together with others, doing yoga together, chanting together, and breathing the same air together is another step toward enlightenment — the ability to live always in the Self and always in the flow of love. Thank you for being one who is teaching me.

Capacity

March 2000

"We are already one. But we imagine that we are not.
And what we have to recover is our original unity.
What we have to be is what we are."

- Thomas Merton

"Within your own house dwells the treasury of joy;
so why do you go begging from door to door?"

- Sufi saying

You have a habitual mood, which you can think of as psychological homeostasis. It is a set-point to which you revert when you're not paying any attention to how you feel. Yoga changes your set-point along with changing your body. Many people are surprised to find they feel better after their first ninety-minute yoga class than after a full night of sleep. Most importantly, this feeling is not merely a physical improvement. It is also a change in your mood, attitude or emotional state. But you must ask yourself, "How long does it last?" When your habitual mood begins to take over again, along with the too-familiar physical tensions, you can simply do more yoga, and you feel wonderful again. The good news is that, as you continue doing yoga, your set-point changes. Then the question becomes, "How good can you allow yourself to feel?"

One day I was walking through our Namaste Department (our reception area) and a man stopped me, "Do you remember me?" He reminded me of his name and then I recognized him, "I have not seen you for a couple of years!" He confessed, "Yes, I was taking classes twice a week for over six months and then I stopped. I have been gone for over two years, but I want you to know that now I am back!" "What happened?" I asked. "I did not realize it at the time," he said, "but I stopped because I could not allow myself to feel that good. I felt better than ever in my whole life, but something in me could not allow that. So I stopped, and I started feeling worse and worse. After two years, I realized that I really do want to feel that good. So I want you to know that I am back! You will see me again, twice a week every week!" We laughed together and I welcomed him back. He came regularly for two or three weeks, and then stopped again. It probably will not take him two years to figure it out this time, and he will be back again — soon, I hope.

What is your capacity? How good can you allow yourself to feel? Some people carry the equivalent of a thimble with them and, when it is full, they are happy. Anything more will not fit in the thimble, so it overflows. The overflow is expressed in tears or laughter, or by depleting yourself through intense personal interactions, or as a sudden burst of activity. One woman told me that she could not come to evening classes because she was unable to go to sleep when she went home. She felt so energized that she would clean her house until midnight. I told her, "You have got a thimble, and it is filled to overflowing. You need a larger capacity. Get a bucket!" Increase your capacity to contain that energy without feeling like you have to deplete yourself again.

As you learn to relax the tensions in your body, both in the outer layers as well as in the core, your capacity expands. It is as though the tight areas in your body are the edges of your container. As they melt, your thimble becomes a bucket. Then you exchange the bucket for a bathtub. What is larger than a bathtub? What do you want your maximum capacity for joy to be? Yoga calls it the ocean. Expand your capacity until you find your set-point in the ocean of consciousness. You will live in the continuing joy of your Self.

Yoga is Skill in Action

February 2000

"Action is nothing but the movement of energy in consciousness,
and it inevitably bears its own fruit."

- Yoga Vasistha

"He who sees inaction in action and action in inaction,
he is intelligent among men; he is a man of established wisdom
and a true performer of all actions."

- The Bhagavad Gita

I sat and watched the *Guru* in the big chair at the front of the room as someone approached with a photo in hand. I knew that this *Guru* usually gestured to a nearby assistant to use the rubber stamp that had been prepared for this purpose. There were several hundred more people still waiting in line. Instead, she took the photo and a pen. She turned her full attention to the photograph and signed her name with a focus and in a meticulous way that I had never observed in anyone doing anything ever before. It emblazoned itself into my memory, and arises inside often, even ten years later.

Several weeks later, I found myself doing some late night deskwork. I was hurrying through the last thing — to address several envelopes. Suddenly, I remembered how she had signed that photo. I decided to address the envelopes the same way. I wrote the first word with my best penmanship, beautifully, meticulously and with great focus. By the time I was halfway through the next word, I was in bliss! I found I could address all the envelopes this way, and even pick up my keys and drive home in this way — and each thing I did added to my ecstasy. Then I understood this line in the <u>Bhagavadgita</u>, "*Yogah karmasu kaushalam*" — Yoga is skill in action.

Do every action to your best possible ability. This does not mean that you have to be good at every thing you do, but merely that you do it as skillfully as possible. Pour yourself into each action, fully and completely. When you do things halfway, then you are only half present. The one who misses out is you. You miss out on the Self! By pouring yourself fully into each and every action, you become fully present — and your own presence is "the bliss of consciousness itself."

This is not the same as doing things well so that others will notice. Then you are focusing on the response you might get, whether from your spouse, your customer or boss, your friend or family member. You are waiting for their response so you can use it to construct a sense of self — an externally constructed sense of self. This is not "skill in action," even if you are performing your task skillfully, because everything is focused on the response instead of on the action itself.

Every action has an inherent perfection. The slow motion replays of football players falling onto the ground show this surprising beauty and grace, almost like dance sequences. Something as simple as unlocking the door, getting into your car, placing your key in the ignition and starting the engine can be done as "skill in action." You will notice a difference. Amazingly, it does not even take more time to do most things this way. But you may find you have less of a need to rush around. Time may take on a quality of timelessness, and life may develop a quality of dimensionality that you are used to finding only in your meditation or your yoga practice. That is because skill in action is yoga.

You do get to practice this technique when you are doing *Svaroopa Yoga* poses. The care and attention you cultivate when you are doing the physical practices are a powerful form of training for how to live your whole life. The opening of your spine draws your attention inward to help you explore the dimensionality of your own being. Then you learn how to take this quality into your whole life with you — yoga is skill in action. Try it!

Commitment

May 2000

"Nothing can come out of nothing."
- William Shakespeare

"The path of liberation is subtle, and hard, and long...
By this path alone the wise attain Consciousness while living."
- Briha-daran-yaka Upanishad

"My boyfriend calls it the 'c' word," a student told me recently. Commitment. You get nothing without commitment. It's even becoming popular in the working world again. A few years ago, the best way to get ahead was job-hopping. Now professional advisors recommend you make a commitment to one job for three to seven years in order to maximize both your personal development and what you can offer your employer.

Commitment means you do it, even when it is hard to do. No "fair weather friend" — you are reliable, consistent, dedicated. I think the best model for commitment is being a parent. My commitment to my children (though they are now adults) is absolute, and always has been. In those early years, it sometimes meant I had to go without sleep in order to meet their needs. Later, it meant I had to give up things I wanted in order to provide for them, whether it was meeting their genuine needs or fulfilling a reasonable number of their desires. I did it, and I got as much as I gave — actually, I got more than I gave. The process of committing myself changed something in me.

Yoga says that you must pair commitment with letting go. There must be a total dedication that has a quality of lightness to it. This type of commitment does not come from a deep unfulfilled need or an insecurity that impels you into fanatical behavior. Whatever you commit to, you follow through on it completely, without depending on its outcome to go a certain predetermined way, because any sense of dependency sets you up for a fall. You do your very best (yoga is skill in action) and then you let it go — like making a paper airplane. You make the best one you can, learning from all your prior attempts, even studying the diagram you found on the Internet. You throw the plane into the air at the best possible angle with just the right amount of force. Then you laugh when it crashes (or flies into the sky!).

This combination of commitment and letting go applies to the practice of yoga also. But you have to sort out which is which! Some people encounter challenging times and let go of their twice-weekly yoga classes or their at-home yoga practice. They call it "letting go" — when what they really need to be letting go of is some other less valuable activity.

Yoga does not work unless you do it. It is like your television — it only works if you turn it on. Your commitment to the practice is what gives you the ability to let go in every area of your life, so you can laugh at whatever happens. You might even find that you have to laugh at how your yoga poses look — but you still do them anyway! This is the perfect combination — commitment while simultaneously letting go of how you think it should look. You may even have to let go of how you think the process should go. Sometimes you progress smoothly from one stage to another, and sometimes it is "two steps forward, one step back." Still you show up and do it.

Commitment to yoga is actually a commitment to your own future. Continuing your yoga practice will guarantee that your body does not age like the average person. You will become progressively healthier and happier than anyone who isn't doing yoga. But the real payoff happens deeper inside — your sense of self plumbs the deeper dimensions of reality. Yoga promises you a progressive unveiling of the light of consciousness within. Now that is something worth committing yourself to!

Finding Happiness

June 2000

"We are already one. But we imagine that we are not.
And what we have to recover is our original unity.
What we have to be is what we are."

- Thomas Merton

"Life, liberty and the pursuit of happiness," declared our Founding Fathers, "is an inalienable right." Pursuing happiness is certainly a theme of modern life. What would America look like today if they had declared our right to "happiness" instead of to the "pursuit of happiness?"

Yoga says that happiness is not enough. Happiness is a fleeting taste of something much greater — bliss. You have experienced it in those incredible moments, the truly fulfilling experiences of complete happiness at various times in your life. Remember the best of them. Look into the moment where you won the race, or you stood overlooking the incredible view, or you held that new baby. In that moment, time does not exist. You experience that vastness and incredible joy again every time you recall that experience. You can bring it up in its fullness again by using your memory. It is incredible! It is truly called "bliss," the bliss of your own Being.

If you do not experience this bliss, you do not feel fully alive. This bliss is your own Being. It is the source of life within you. You must experience bliss again and again, or life has no meaning. So, yes — you must pursue happiness. But you will find it inside, not outside.

The problem with pursuing happiness on the outside is that you must postpone it. In order to pursue happiness, you have to attach it to some future event or some object you currently do not have. It has to be in your future. The new home or the vacation trip will make you happy later — not now. And you have to work hard for it, or it depends on another person, but you cannot be happy now because you do not have the thing you need in order to be happy. You're ignoring your own bliss-essence in order to wait for a future moment when you can be happy.

Where is it that you are looking for happiness these days? Wherever you look, you actually already expect that the happiness you get will be temporary. When you get that something you are pursuing, it will make you happy for a while, only until there is another something to be pursued. I remember a friend in the *ashram* (residential yoga center) when I was studying in India. Every time she wanted something that she could not get, she put it on her list. She listed everything and planned to get it at some point in the future. A year after returning to the U.S., she told me, "I got everthing on my list." I asked, "Are you happy?" She said, "No. I have another list."

I recently asked the students in a meditation class if anyone had ever gotten all their ducks in a row. Did you ever get everything in your life set up perfectly? One lady answered yes. I asked, "How long did it last?" To my amazement she said, "Four months." Then she added, "But I was not happy. I thought I was going to be, but I was not." Happiness is not outside of you. Happiness is not inside of you. Happiness *is* you! When you feel happy, you're experiencing a taste of your Self. Stop looking outside. Do more yoga.

Balance

July 2000

"The first rule is to keep an untroubled spirit. The second is to look things in the face and know them for what they are."

- Marcus Aurelius

"If you are inwardly free from fighting, no one will be able to start a fight with you."

- Anonymous

CR

I cannot believe those two weeks of vacation balance out fifty weeks of work every year. Besides, most full time jobs are not forty hours per week anymore — they are fifty or sixty hours, even at a yoga foundation! If balance is the goal, most of us are failing miserably. Fortunately, yoga is not about balance, it is about integration.

Balance means that you need some recovery time after a hectic day, so perhaps you have a glass of wine, or a nap on the couch, or a couple of hours of stupid television shows. Balance means you spent a lot of time with people, so you need some private time to make up for it. Balance means that you spend a lot of time doing things for others, so now you expect them to do nice things for you – or you go spend lots of money on yourself instead. Balance is compensation: getting something to make up for how hard it was or how bad you feel. What is it that makes you feel bad, anyway?

Integration means that you have an inner reservoir that sustains you through-out your hectic day, so you do not feel exhausted when you get home. Integra-tion means you don't get lost in other people's ideas of who you are, even when you are with them all day long. So, now you do not need the private time to reconstruct your sense of self. Integration means you do things for others out of the inner fullness, which loves to serve and loves to share. Now you do not need for them to make it up to you. Integration means you make choices about what to buy based on clarity and purpose instead of need, greed or compensation for feeling bad. Integration means you take your Self with you wherever you go.

We include training in integration at the end of every yoga class. The purpose of the contemplation is to help you carry yoga into your life. *Yoga Mudra*, the energy seal at the end of class, is to "top off your tank," so that you carry that inner fullness with you. Even the guided awareness in *Shavasana*, "Notice your toes…" helps with integration: the interweaving of your awareness through your body and, ultimately, through your whole life.

Yoga does give you balance, though it is a completely different kind. It is inner balance. Your own inner sense of yourself is found in a deep center that is always balanced. Nothing can topple you, because you are anchored so deep in your core. That essence of Being is your support. You are like an ice skater that leaps, twirls and lands on one foot, because there is an inner sense of balance that does not depend on the outer circumstances. Life is no longer a balancing act; it becomes a beautiful expression of your inner essence.

Find your balance point inside. Anchor your sense of self in your core. Let the inner Reality be your support. Then you will not *need* that two weeks of vacation to make up for the fifty weeks of struggle, but you will really enjoy it!

Vitality

August 2000

*"Vitality shows in not only the ability to persist,
but in the ability to start over."*

- F. Scott Fitzgerald

"You can sense energy to the degree your heart is open and loving."

- Sanaya Roman

CR

If you want to understand vitality, spend the afternoon following a three-year-old child around. Where does that inexhaustible energy come from!? You were actually like that once, yourself. Now, if you keep yourself going all day long, it is probably caffeine that is your fuel — or maybe sheer adrenaline. This is not vitality. It ends in exhaustion. This is not a tiredness that feels good. It is a feeling of nervous exhaustion and being mentally drained.

So, you come to yoga class or do some practice at home, and your cup runneth over. The energy of life itself fills you to the brim, and maybe even overflows in easy laughter with yoga friends after class. You take this vitality into your life, but your activities and relationships seem to drain you again. Then, you need another yoga class. This is a repetitive cycle, but at least you have a way of filling yourself up again.

However, yoga says that energy is limitless. Your supply is not limited. In the beginning of yoga, you fill your cup each time you practice. Yet, something more begins to happen. Yoga practice, especially the experiences of deep inner absorption, connects you into the Source. Then you no longer merely carry a cupful of energy. When I first experienced this, it felt like I suddenly had an umbilical cord attached to a fire hydrant, drawing the energy from an inexhaustible Source. It is impossible to deplete this Source, though you are able to cut yourself off from it. Yoga shows you how to live in a way that keeps you always connected.

It is not actually your physical activities that are so draining — it is your thoughts. You go each day to the same job and return home again. You deal with the same family members over and over. Then, yoga changes the way you see them. Instead of being unhappy with the way things are going, your mind begins to see the best in every situation. Old negative thoughts disappear, and you begin to savor memories of the sweetest moments of your life. Worries about the future drop away so you can notice the beauty in the moment. The _Katha Upanishad_ promises that your mind becomes your best friend instead of your worst enemy.

When your mind is beautiful like this, then your body does not tighten up. Consider how much energy it takes to sustain constant muscular tension. That energy can be used for other things when your body is always open and relaxed. Consider how much energy is wasted in reviewing the unchangeable past and the unpredictable future, when you could be vitally alive and present in the moment! Rumi says, "You have the energy of the sun in you, but you keep knotting it up at the base of your spine."

Yoga practice becomes not merely a way of recovering from the drain of the day, but a way of opening to the inner source of life itself. There is a fountain of life filling you from the inside, if you just quit clamping down on it. Begin at the tailbone in order to open it up. Then do it again. You will discover how to live in an entirely new way — always open. Your mind will be your friend. The energy of life itself will pour through your eyes and heart, and fill into your relationships and your life. And you may discover that yoga offers even more. Do more yoga!

Renewal

September 2000

*"You have everything. You are the whole world. Why?
Because the kingdom of God is within you.
Then why do you want to run about and beg?"*

- Yoga Swami

"Make yourself new by diving into your inner Source."

- Rama Berch

"Reduce – Reuse – Recycle" is the message emblazoned on my insulated mug, which is scratched and nicked precisely because I follow its message. It is showing its age. You might be feeling the same way. A generation or two ago, people took for granted that they would develop some aches and pains as they aged. Baby Boomers like myself are less accepting of the rusty joints and leaky mind. Many young adults say they aren't going to wait until their hinges begin to squeak. And now there is an upsurge of interest in yoga for kids.

The yoga texts say, "Begin yoga as a youth. Do not wait until your hair and teeth are falling out and you cannot see any more. Start now! Do not waste your life." But what if you did not do that? What about these aches and pains? What about those wrinkles? Yoga makes you young again. Young eyes shine with light. They are wide open and clear. Young skin is soft and smooth. The young mind is osmotic – able to absorb new information at an extraordinary rate. Yoga promises you all of this, and more. Over 2,000 medical studies show that yoga and meditation reverse the aging process. This is fantastic news, but it is still not what I call "renewal". Renewal is to make new again — a change throughout your whole being, not just your body and mind.

Do you remember your first love? There might be a whole movie of material in your story, especially about what happened at the end, but forget that for the moment. Do you remember the feeling of being in love for the first time? This is what yoga calls "new." Maturity brings a lot of other things along with love, like responsibility, mutual support and compromise. But that feeling of newness is still in there, sometimes buried under other stuff. Finding it again is called renewal.

But renewal is not limited to love. The day can be exhausting, so you fall into bed. You hope to wake in the morning refreshed and renewed. Sometimes it works, and sometimes it doesn't. *Shavasana* is more reliable, the guided relaxation at the beginning and end of yoga classes. Students often describe going really deep and feeling more refreshed than after a full night of sleep. Their eyes are shining. Their skin is smooth. They are renewed. Where is this "really deep" place that provides such renewal?

The source is within you. You tap into it when you allow yourself to feel love, or you get a good sleep. You tap into it every time you laugh. It bubbles up every time your mind becomes still. When you live in this flow of aliveness and bliss, you are always new. When you cut it off, you begin to die. Even a moment of this connection is a renewal. Yoga is the science of connecting.

Yoga first "youthens" your body, giving increased flexibility and resilience along with lessening your aches and pains. It then helps you with your mind, providing clarity and a renewed enthusiasm for life. You develop an emotional bounce, so the events of life do not flatten you. But the best is when you keep going — a whole new sense of Self arises from the Source inside. Then, regard-less of what your odometer says about the number of years on this body, you live each day as fully new. No renewal is needed. Allow yoga to make you new again.

Seeing Past the Illusion

October 2000

"Oh friend, where are you going?
Where have you come from, and what are you supposed to do?
You belong to the supreme Truth, but you have forgotten your origin.
Now is the time to get back on the main road."

- Muktananda

"The height of all philosophy is to know thyself;
and the end of this knowledge is to know God."

- Francis Quarles

There is only one light shining through every person's eyes. When you look into that light, your mind falls silent. The two of you share that One light and melt into a profound experience. It happens every time you allow it to happen. You do not even have to wait for just that one special person, because it happens with every person. The Light of Consciousness is there in everyone. All you have to do is see it!

It's all an illusion. Nothing really exists. Do not get caught up in the world. It is not Real. It is fickle, constantly changing. The constant changes mean that you cannot rely on anything. You are ultimately alone. So, give up everything external and find that One Reality within yourself. When you find That, you discover that nothing really exists. There is only One and you are That.

By now, I hope you are feeling confused by the contradictions in the two passages above. Yoga says both of these things: everything shines with the light of consciousness AND that it is all illusion. Both are true. Both are true at the same time. It merely depends on what you are looking at.

It is like going to the movies. The story played out on the screen is not real. It is a caricature of life, and the images are greater-than-life-size. When they show a close up of someone's face, it is two stories tall! You can go to the movie and get so caught up in the story that it echoes in your mind for days. Or you can watch the movie, laugh and cry, and walk out knowing it was merely good entertainment. It is up to you.

The real movie plays in your mind. The conscious energy that becomes everything that exists plays out the comedy and drama of life on the screen of your mind. So you keep running movies through your mind. Sometimes you even play reruns of your life. This means you are looking at the illusion instead of the ever-present Reality. Your thoughts and memories are images that keep you from seeing what is in front of you.

You must look past the illusion to see things as they are. Then, you will see that everything is made of that one conscious energy. Even your mind is made of that One, and can actually be used to help take you back to the knowing and living of that One in every moment.

We celebrate the illusion in a great festival of assumed identity, Halloween. You can be anyone you want to be, for just one day. It is great fun! If you can have that much fun being someone else for a day, imagine how much fun Consciousness is having, being everyone all the time! Now, all you have to do is see past the illusion and know the Reality within all forms, even you!

Family

November 2000

"*When we enter into any relationship with the premise that we are empty and the other person will fill us in, we are sure to fail. We can only win when we proceed from wholeness.*"

- Alan Cohen

"*There is no way to take the danger out of human relationships.*"

- Barbara G. Harrison

One of the primary causes of holiday stress is family. Yet those without family often experience severe holiday depression. How can both be true?

Your family exists for the purpose of pushing your buttons. They are really good at it, are they not? They show you exactly how you are not yet enlightened. They do you a great service. If no one came along to show you where these hot spots were, you could continue on in your comfortable delusions. You would continue utilizing your familiar and effective ways of avoiding facing yourself. Few friends will take on that level of commitment and responsibility, because it is too easy to end a friendship. Family ties can be ignored but not broken. This family tie creates an incredible trust, even when the relationships are difficult. This trust allows you to dislike (even sometimes to hate) one another while there is an underlying love, recognized or unrecognized.

Psychology is well known for offering tools that identify the causes of our hangups, often found in our childhood experiences. Students sometimes share with me the difficulties of their childhood and how those events caused their current misery. Yoga offers a way to reframe that experience — your childhood was your *karma*. You were born into the perfect family for you to undergo significant and key experiences necessary to fulfill your *karma*. Your family did not create that *karma*. You did. You set events into motion, even in a previous lifetime. Those events will reach their full flowering at your own doorstep. You can blame no one else for your *karma*, only yourself, even if you do not remember setting the events into motion.

Spiritual growth means you: (1) take responsibility for everything that happened to you, (2) drop it and forget about it, and (3) move on with your life. You create new *karma* by making new choices, based on a different understanding than the one you constructed through those *karma*-rich years of your childhood. Yoga gives you this new understanding, bit by bit.

I met a man a few days ago that came in for his first yoga experience. As we talked, he mentioned the company he works for. I know one of the executives in his company because he practices yoga at MYA. I asked, "Do you know this man? He takes classes here." "Oh, yes!" replied the new student. "I bet I can tell you how long he has been taking yoga. Let's see, about four years, right?

He used to be really tightly wound, but that changed about four years ago. He is really calmed down and is much easier to deal with." Yoga gives you this new understanding so tangibly that they even notice it at work. What about with your family?

Now, you might be thinking, "If only my family members would practice yoga. My life would be so much easier!" While that is true, it is another attempt to abdicate your responsibility to face yourself and your own *karma*. If you do yoga, your family might change or they might not. But you will change the way you look at them, how you think of them, how you speak of them, the way you speak to them, and the way you act toward them. That change in you is what matters the most, and it does change your *karma*!

Perhaps the ultimate test of your yogic attainment is to spend time with your family over the holidays. You may find that you can maintain your hold on sanity for days longer than ever before. After more yoga, you may begin to carry a quality of inner peace within you without having to strain for it. In succeeding years, it gets better until it becomes a persistent quality of genuine love and delight in the familiar family antics that used to drive you crazy. Surely that means you are getting close to enlightenment! Do more yoga.

'Tis the Season of Giving

December 2000

"Most of the joy of living comes out of true giving—giving without strings attached."

— Gary Emery

"It has all become so commercial! The spirit of the season is lost. I remember when..." The focus of the holidays is undeniably on gifts. The real meaning gets buried under the wrapping paper and ribbons, followed by the credit card bills the following month. Why do we go through this every year?

Look again. Look closely at your own experience. There is a real bliss in the giving of gifts (as well as in receiving them!). There is nothing wrong with having a holiday that is focused on giving gifts to people we cherish. We can prompt an experience of joy for them, while we delight in our own generosity and caring. The giving of gifts is even mentioned in a yoga text as a reliable way to experience bliss. However, the *Bhagavadgita* tells us that there are three types of gifts: pure gift, uncaring gift, or the gift given with ulterior motives.

The pure (*sattvic*) gift is given with only one thought, "It is to be given." You really enjoy giving this kind of gift. It goes to someone you care about and want to give a gift to. You really look forward to sharing their delight in it, because you know it is perfect for her or him (and it was the perfect price!).

The uncaring (*tamasic*) gift is one given without thought, or given to a person you dislike or disrespect. You put nothing of yourself into it, so it has no aliveness. There is no joy in it. It can even be expensive or impressive, but there is no real meaning because you did not put yourself into it. Your joy comes from getting it over with, completing the task.

The gift given with ulterior motives (*rajasic*) is one you choose for its effect. The recipient will be impressed, or perhaps they will owe you something once it is opened. There can be joy in this, but it is not an uplifting feeling at all. The joy comes from a feeling of having won a competition, with an undercurrent of fear because you know the contest is really never over.

Ultimately your experience of this holiday season is dependent on why you give the gifts, not what you select. It is about your motivation. Why you do things is always more important than what you do. Your motivation determines your experience more than the actual deed.

"What can I get for so-and-so?" The pressures of the season show up so clearly when you make up your gift list, especially if you plan a budget amount for each person. How do you decide who should be on your list and what to give to each one? This is very tricky stuff! And you must decide. This is the yoga of life.

ॐ

The Power of Language

January 2001

"Words are the most powerful thing in the universe...
Words are containers.
They contain faith, or fear, and they produce after their kind."

- Charles Capps

"We are held accountable for the very words which we speak...
By our words we are justified or condemned."

- Ernest Holmes

CR

The universe arises from one sound, according to St. John. "In the beginning was the Word…" Yoga says that *Om* is that primordial sound from which everything has arisen. Theoretical astrophysicists detail the effects of the Big Bang in milliseconds, citing a progression arising first as sound, then the emanation of light, the beginning of time and the expansion of space. *Om* is that vibration that manifested first as sound. It still vibrates through everything that exists and beyond. When we chant *Om*, we approximate the sound, though it is actually heard in its pristine power in the quiet inner spaces of meditation, reverberating in the space inside your heart.

The one sound split itself into many sounds, fragmenting into separate vibra-tions that then became and are still becoming the many separate things. This process by which the formless manifests this astounding array of multiplicity is named *matrka* in Sanskrit. *Matrka* is like a prism held in the beam of sunlight, splintering the one ray of light into a rainbow of colors. *Matrka* splinters the one sound into many sounds, like A, M, L, SH, etc. We combine these sounds in various ways to form words. Then we use the words to tie ourselves up in knots!

The knots in your body are actually created by your mind. You already know that you can think yourself into exhaustion. You create tremendous layers of physical tensions with your thoughts every day. It is not the words you say to other people that have the most power — it is the words you use on yourself. The repetitive thoughts, especially the ones that you would never admit, create bindings that lock up your body and even limit your life. More powerful are the hidden levels that create unrecognized patterns through your whole life. Many people choose to undergo hypnosis or to see a therapist to uncover and name these hidden bindings. The power of doing yoga, meditating and studying *Sanskrit* is that you can completely clear them away.

The power of Sanskrit is that it reverses the process of *matrka*. By studying the sounds and learning the terms, you begin to untie the knots that you didn't know you had. Sanskrit is the language of yoga. It is a specialized language that communicates the principles of yoga and describes the profound inner levels of experience. English is also a specialized language, arising from a dialect of German that was spoken by the merchants. English is a language of trade, of economics, of barter. It has an influence on your mind that can even affect your relationships, leading to the cost-benefit analysis — am I getting enough for everything I give to this person?

When you steep your mind in the sounds and words of Sanskrit, the vibration frees you from the barter mentality. This metamorphosis is the goal of all yoga practices. However, the poses alone may not be enough to deal with some of your most deeply imbedded mental patterns. This is why we play Sanskrit chants as background music in our classes. The beauty of the language acts as a subliminal yoga, emptying the hidden recesses of your thoughts as you clear the tensions from your body. When you take the chants home or play them in your car, yoga continues to work on you without you having to "do" anything.

Namaste

February 2001

"I honor the place in you where the entire universe dwells.
I honor the place in you that is love, truth, light and peace.
When you are in that place in you
and I am in that place in me,
we are one."

— attributed to Ram Dass

All of yoga's teachings are contained in this one word. *Namaste.* Your experience at the end of each class is more than mere relaxation, an experience of something beyond words. This inner experience is the point of this greeting, *Namaste.* When you speak this to another person, it reminds you of the deeper dimension of your own being. It is a way of naming the unnamable. It simultaneously addresses that deeper dimension of the one you greet. As hard as it can be to remember the Namaste Place in yourself, sometimes it is even harder to see it in others.

The biggest challenges in life come from relationships. Sometimes it is a family member or friend, while other times it is simply the driver in the car beside yours, but it is a relationship nonetheless. The most important factor in all these relationships is you. This is the good news because you are the only one you can hope to have any control over. All the schemes and strategies to control others, to straighten them out, to put them on the right track, to show them once and for all, or to help them finally get it — they are all doomed to failure. Because even if your manipulation succeeds, there will be something else that bugs you. You can even go as far as to change your life around to get rid of the people that disturb you the most, by changing jobs or even changing spouses. But there will still be something that bugs you, even in the new people in your life.

Looking within to find your Namaste Place is essential, but it is only a beginning. You must begin to see that everyone has that Namaste Place. There is one light shining through every person's eyes; one Self has become the Self of all. This is what you recognize when you look deep into someone's eyes. You just have to remember to look.

You have been trained to look only at the surface level. In interactions with others, you probably look at their hair, their body and clothes. You watch their lips as they talk. You focus on their behavior, obsess on their words, structure your whole life around their desires. You replay old conversations in your mind and structure "what-ifs" endlessly. Stop! Look into their eyes — not at the surface of their eyes, but really look, inside. There is something irresistible there. It is there in your loved ones. It is there in everyone. Sometimes it is actually easier to see it in a stranger than in someone close to you.

Where is the Namaste Place in you? There is a place of love and truth, light and peace, a place where the entire universe dwells. The person next to you has a Namaste Place. Look for it. Look beyond the surface. You do not have to wait for them to find it before you see it. You can acknowledge it even if they do not know. The result is a change in you, and that is the only change that matters.

Vegetarian

March 2001

*"Do not to others what you do not wish done to yourself;
and wish for others too what you desire and long for, for yourself —
this is the whole of righteousness, heed it well."*

- Mahabharata

"Animals are my friends — and I don't eat my friends."

- George Bernard Shaw

CR

When I quit eating meat twenty-five years ago, there were not many alternatives available. There were not even many health food stores. Now you can even buy vegetarian frozen dinners! Most restaurants offer several vegetarian selections. I used to be able to order only a salad and baked potato. Fortunately, I like baked potatoes. I was on the cutting edge, even considered a little weird. "You are a vegetarian? What *do* you eat?" These days it is not a big deal. Becoming a vegetarian is even applauded as a healthy lifestyle choice.

People become vegetarians for many different reasons. Many are cutting out red meat for health reasons or simply to lose weight. Others want to make a political statement about the meat industry. Social responsibility makes some people concerned about the world economy; "So many people are starving. The grain that feeds the cattle would feed so many more thousands of people." The negative ecological impact has been well documented. Some people have eliminated all animal flesh but still eat seafood. Others have cut out meat in order to save money.

Why would a yogi become a vegetarian? *Ahimsa.* It is the first of the five *yamas* (restraints), which are yoga's practices to clean up your lifestyle. Each *yama* teaches a way to make your life into a more tangible reflection of your highest principles, by eliminating the things that drag you down. The first *yama, ahimsa,* is non-harming. When you begin to practice *ahimsa,* you first identify the harmful things you do. Then you simply refrain from doing them. This includes the sharp words you fling at another person, as well as some of your less-than-admirable driving habits. You may even find that some physical violence needs to be stopped, whether that is hitting the dog, spanking the children, hitting another adult, or pounding your fist on tables or into walls. Another primary practice of *ahimsa* is to not cause the death of an animal in order to fill your stomach.

Everything you have heard about hormones in meat is true. They do have an effect on your mind as well as your body. A natural outgrowth of eliminating meat and fish from your diet is that you become less anxious and less aggressive. You can finally learn the difference between assertive and aggressive. You learn to speak out without being angry. You begin to communicate directly but with love. You begin to live with less habitual nervousness and become less inclined to frustration and impatience. All this happens from just changing your diet.

Yet none of this is why yogis gravitate toward vegetarianism. You may even have found that you have changed your diet since you began yoga without realizing why. It often happens naturally. Yoga reliably gives you the experience of the deeper inner Reality. In this level of your own Beingness, you are that One that pervades all. One of the very first experiences I had in yoga made this real for me. I felt my body expand to become the whole universe. I felt the grasses growing out of my skin like the hairs on my arms. The skies were in my eyes, the rivers were the blood flowing through my veins. I saw the animals as my own being in many forms, and I knew I could never eat meat again. Later, I discovered a passage in the *Vedas* that describes this as how the universe was created.

When you see with these new eyes, you cannot bring yourself to harm another, not even an animal, because they are all glorious expressions of the One (which is you). This profound reverence for all life permeates your whole life. *Patanjali* describes in the <u>*Yoga Sutras*</u> that one who is established in *ahimsa* exudes an incredible peace, so profound that no one around them can feel any type of hostility. The lion lies down with the lamb.

You do not have to become a vegetarian to practice yoga. Yoga will give you such profound benefits that it really does not matter what you eat. But if you are finding yourself drawn toward a different diet, this may help you recognize why. And you probably need to learn about a balanced vegetarian diet. There are many vegetarian cookbooks that will help you learn how to eat in a whole new way. It is even possible that the confirmed carnivores will find a recipe or two that they enjoy!

Self-Effort & Grace

April 2001

"Grace strikes us when
we are in great pain and restlessness.
It strikes us when we walk through the dark valley
of a meaningless and empty life."

- Paul Tillich

"The way of grace is mysterious.
You struggle for it and you do not get it.
Sometimes, without any struggle you get it.
Its working is governed by something beyond all laws.
It is not bound by any rules, regulations or conditions."

- Papa Ramdas

You must put up the sail in order to catch the wind. If you do not do your part, you will not get anywhere. *Tapas* is the *Sanskrit* word for self-effort. *Tapas* means you have to invest yourself. You get nothing unless you apply yourself. You cannot finish school without *tapas*. It takes *tapas* to buy a home or to have a successful relationship. You give up some things in order to get others. Just going through the motions is not enough.

A student asked recently, "You mean I should turn off my television when I do my yoga?" Yes. Yoga is more than poses — it affects your state of mind. That is yoga's real purpose! Most people already recognize that they need help with their minds. Compare the state you are in after yoga class to your state after watching a television movie. Consider what it is that you really want. There are so many things you can do, and only a limited amount of available time. *Tapas* is making a choice. You are always giving up something when you are choosing something else.

Technically, *tapas* means heat, the heat generated by friction. This is the friction of your ego rubbing against God. When you are making a choice, choose that which will take you closer to God. You might find that you have to give up some old self-defeating habits, though it can be difficult because you are so attached to them.

Our culture worships self indulgence. *Tapas* is sacrifice. You give up some things in order to get others. *Tapas* makes you strong. *Tapas* gives you a strong body, a clear mind, the ability to make decisions and stick to them. *Tapas* is New Year's resolutions. How are you coming on yours? If you did not make any, stop for a moment now. Take a good look at yourself and see if there are any ways that you would like to improve yourself. Make at least one resolution — if not for the year, at least try it for one week.

Grace is the wind in the sail. You have to haul the sail up, but you don't have to row. With *tapas*, you figure out which effort to put forth. You make the decision to raise the sail instead of taking out the oars. If the wind is light, you use a different sail than if it is strong. And you keep an eye on it as you move along, adjusting it to make the best use of the natural fuel — the wind is free. Grace is the ultimate fuel, both in the world as well as in your spiritual development. Grace makes things easy.

Yoga is the science of Grace. You open up your body and quiet your mind so that you can tune into grace, the force that flows from your own subtle and blissful inner Source. You know what it feels like when you come up from the final *Shavasana* in your yoga class; there is more light shining in your eyes. Everyone around you benefits from that glow. You return home or go on with your day, powered by an inner force that shines through every activity and every relationship. Grace softens your edges and opens your heart. *Tapas* makes you able to hold the grace.

The milk of a lioness can only be held in a container made of pure gold. If you put the milk of a lioness in a cup made of any other material, it eats through the container and leaks out. Only gold can hold this strong milk. *Tapas* makes you into pure gold, so you can live your life full of grace.

Change

May 2001

"The world never stands still. It is a constant becoming."
- Robert Collier

"Enlightenment is not an attainment; it is a realization.
When you wake up, everything changes and nothing changes.
If a blind man realizes that he can see, has the world changed?"
- Dan Millman

CR

It is always easier to go through a change when you are the one initiating it. To quit your job is a very different experience than being fired; to end a relationship or move to a new city is easier when you make the choice than when someone else does. What is the yoga of change?

The _Pratyabhijnahrdayam_ describes the world as being an expression of one unchanging Reality expressing itself in many forms, which are in ever-constant movement and change. That one Reality lies at the foundation of your being as your own essence; consciousness itself as your "Self." Yoga is the science of finding that, inside. When you have not yet become stabilized in it, change can rock you to the core.

You have a number of options for how to handle change, whether it is a change in your yoga classes or a change in your life. Some of the options are familiar. You can:

1. Complain, blame, resist, and/or withdraw. You can say, "He said, she said, I do not know who but somebody said..." You can undercut all efforts to improve your experience, and even sabotage the process. You have probably already tried one of these techniques at some time in your life.
2. Step back on the sidelines and wait quietly (but not patiently) for the dust to clear, hoping that things turn out in a way you like.
3. Continue on as though nothing is changing, like an ostrich with its head in the sand. Then you can be righteously indignant when it affects you.
4. Go somewhere else that doesn't have so much going on, so you can feel "safe".
5. Just "kibitz". This is one of my personal favorites. I learned it as a child, watching family members playing cards, and offering my opinion of what they should do with the cards in _their_ hand.

The problem is that the cards are not in _their_ hand. The cards are in _your_ hand. You have a right to say what happens next. This is not the time to be sitting in full Lotus Pose, meditating on your navel. Play the game!

One of my favorite teaching stories is about the *Guru* who took his young disciples into the nearby park and said, "Let's play baseball." They chose up teams and the first team went up to bat. After scoring five runs, they were put out and the other team prepared to go up to bat. Just then, the *Guru* said, "Let's play soccer!" Now what? Do you moan, "But the other team is ahead. Can't we have a chance to catch up?" Life is not a competition! It is a divine play, and you are here to have experiences, as well as to see through them to the greater Reality beyond. I invite you to play the game. When you participate, you have a better chance of getting what you want. And every experience of life will draw you closer to living in the knowing of the Reality within.

Support

June 2001

"Do what you can, with what you have, where you are."

\- Theodore Roosevelt

"The giver is greater than the gift."

\- Eknath Easwaran

This primary principle of *Svaroopa Yoga* is often expressed in the phrase, "Support equals release." When you put that extra blanket underneath your knee or learn how to stand by leaning into your bones, you experience the reliable and extraordinary release of internal tensions. This creates that delicious feeling of openness and freedom that extends through your body and beyond. The corresponding mental and emotional tensions melt away, and that deeper dimension of your own essence shines through your eyes, fills your body and extends into your life — all from support.

The effects of support are not limited to the body. Support works its magic in relationships, as well. I am sure you can tell the difference between pressure and support when you are the receiver of such attentions from the significant people in your life. In difficult times, would you rather that your loved ones give you support or pressure? However, to discern the fine line between support and pressure when you are the one who is offering is another matter. For this, you have to let go of your version of the script and let the others in your life write their own destiny. Offer support that will help them find clarity about who they are and what they need to do in their life. Figure out how your love and support can speed and smooth their process of blossoming into the most fragrant flower that only they can be. Support makes a big difference.

The same applies to your yoga teacher. While we teachers have chosen to make our work an offering of support to others, there are times that we need your support. Your continuing presence is already an important form of support. Your participation and the accumulated power of your yoga practice provide the field in which your teacher can plant yoga's seeds. Then you can watch both their growth and ultimate harvest in the beauty of your own blossoming. Your payment for those classes makes many things possible, including the physical facility as well as your teachers' abilities to provide for the necessities of their own lives (and maybe a few luxuries?).

In addition, your questions offer support to your teacher, providing opportunities to expand the base of teachings offered. Your enthusiasm and personal stories of yoga's profound effect feed your teacher's heart and soul. Your gratitude inspires them to give their life even more fully to yoga. Thus they are further uplifted by their own practice, as well as inspired by their own gratitude to the teachers who have preceded them on the path.

In times of change, it is easy to go find your own version of "the cave" to hide in. But that may actually be a withdrawal of your support. Your teacher cannot make it happen without you. I am reminded of a phrase that moved me in the '60's, "What if they gave a war and nobody came?" Well, what if your teacher gave a yoga class, and nobody came? After a few attempts, there could not be a class any more.

Teachers offered yoga for free in ancient India. In modern American, you have to pay for your classes. There is a reason for this difference — in ancient India, the teachers were renunciants. They decided they did not want their own home, a car (camel?), a family, or a summer vacation. They gave up everything and devoted their whole life to the study and practice of yoga in all its varieties and increasing subtleties. They were (and are) the most revered members in their culture and society. People support them by providing them with free housing, by bringing them meals every day, and by providing them with free medical care and all the other needs of human life, so the yogis can give their teachings for free.

In America, no one has approached me recently to offer me a free home, meals, or medical care, or a building in which to teach. I must pay for these. The culture of America combined with modern economic realities means that your yoga class must have ten or twenty people in it in order to survive. Now, you must decide if those other people in your (necessarily) larger classes are intruders or if they are a form of support.

Ultimately, anyone who is practicing yoga is potentially one of the most wonderful people you could ever hope to know. If you get to know them, and if you work with them to provide support, your teachers will thrive and will be able to support you. Isn't it wonderful that we cannot do this alone? We must do this together.

Please consider how you want to support your yoga teachers. Maybe it will be by continuing to come to class and by offering your questions, your suggestions, your energy and support. Or you may be able to offer more. We need your support in order to be able to serve you. Thank you.

Who Am I?

July 2001

"Look within. Within is your fountain of good."

- Marcus Aurelius

"We go here, there, to this place, to that one,
always looking for the happiness that is there inside."

- Swami Satchidananda

The toughest commute I ever had was fifteen feet long. One bedroom was my home office. I closed the door each afternoon to go into the family room and become "Mom" again. The transition time between the two me's wasn't long enough without the accustomed thirty-minute drive. It was the first time I realized how completely engrossing an identity can be. It was the beginning of my training in yoga philosophy, though I did not find yoga until two years later. In English we have only one word to translate two different *Sanskrit* words, *atman* and *ahamkara*. We call them both "self." *Atman* is your essence of Being, the deeper Reality, existence-itself being you. We call this Self with a capital "S." *Ahamkara* is your constructed sense of self, the superficial persona, the ever-changing identity that draws its temporary reality from your activities, that we call "self."

Compare it to the ocean. The waves are the ever-moving superficial "self," and your true identity is the whole ocean. The true "Self" is the ocean of consciousness, but you do not yet know it. This not-knowing is the source of all suffering and pain. Since you don't have the deep knowing of the vast Beingness that is the true Self, you look around for something to be — then you *Velcro* yourself to what you do, where you live, who you know, etc. Yoga peels off the *Velcro* so you can know the Self. Yoga makes you able to live in the knowingness and to express it through your life, while you still have a life. You use your multiple identities without being stuck in them.

When life is difficult, it is because you have lost the Self. You are *Velcro*-ed to one of your multiple identities, and your whole sense of self is being threatened. When you were playing in the sandbox and someone took your toy truck or bucket, you ran to your mommy in tears. But now, those toys have little significance because you play in a larger sandbox. Now, leave the sandbox behind and go into the ocean. In the midst of stuff, ask yourself, "Who am I?" When life tosses you around on the waves of the storm, you have to go deeper. Dive like a submarine. This does not mean that you withdraw or isolate yourself. From the depths of the ocean, you can still see the waves. By deepening into your Self, you can experience everything that life offers, without getting lost in it.

"Who am I?" Your answer is a statement, "I am (fill in the blank)." Anything you fill into that blank is limited and subject to change. If you answer with your profession, "I am a yoga teacher," that describes only part of you, based on your activities, and may change at some point in the future. If your answer is based on your relationships, "I am a mother," it is still a limited truth that has not always been true. Instead you could say, "I am a musician / skier / licensed California driver / etc." If you take all of your answers and put them together, you still don't have the whole.

I had some friends who liked jigsaw puzzles. They would have a big puzzle spread out on the coffee table and everyone would work on it for weeks. When it was completed, they mounted it on a board and hung it on the wall. Their hallway was lined with beautiful pictures of the Grand Canyon, an autumn forest, and a snowy mountain cap, but all the pictures were broken up with these squiggly little lines. Pulling the multiple pieces of yourself together like a jigsaw puzzle is like this. There is something more, something that makes it whole. You must find this dimension of your being, or you will always feel fragmented inside.

There are three primary reasons that most people begin yoga:

1. Pain is a great motivator. Yoga excels at freeing you from pain, whether physical, mental or emotional.
2. Yoga is well known for relaxation and for reliable stress relief. Your first class makes you feel more relaxed than ever before. Each class makes you less susceptible to stress, even in difficult circumstances.
3. Your body needs to move. Flexibility, stretching and exercise may have gotten you started in yoga or be tempting you now. In *Svaroopa Yoga*, we open and move your spine, giving you back the flexibility, resilience and stamina that you enjoyed as a youth.

All of these reasons are variations on the theme, "How am I?" Yoga answers that question by making you feel better, no matter how you felt when you arrived. Every time you do yoga, whether in class or on your own, you feel better on all levels and in all ways. But this is not the real purpose of yoga.

A few people start yoga for a fourth reason:

4. "There must be more to life, because this is not enough." This existential angst is reaching epidemic proportions in the USA. A few of you recognize this underlying itch in your life and look to yoga for an answer.

186

This reason is the asking of the question, "Who am I?" You have a good life, even if there are still a few things you are working on. Your family and your job may not be perfect, but they are still wonderful (in some surprising ways). You are beginning to realize that you can tinker with the externals forever and still never get it right. Ultimately, all of that stuff doesn't matter. Because those things do not define you. You are much more.

Let yoga help you answer, "Who am I?" instead of "How am I?" Yoga gives you the answer maybe in that closing *Shavasana* at the end of every class. It is most directly accessed through meditation, which eliminates the middleman of doing poses and other techniques. Even when you think you cannot find it, yoga brings the Self up on the inside. You get good at letting yourself be overwhelmed by the true Self and living in the bliss of your own Being. It pours through you and expresses as joy and love everywhere you go. Do more yoga!

How Am I?

August 2001

*"Happiness is the realization of God in the heart.
Happiness if the result of praise and thanksgiving, of faith,
of acceptance, a quiet tranquil realization of the love of God."*
- White Eagle

*"If you want happiness for an hour—take a nap.
If you want happiness for a day—go fishing.
If you want happiness for a month—get married.
If you want happiness for a year—inherit a fortune.
If you want happiness for a lifetime—help someone else.
If you want eternal happiness—know yourself."*
- Chinese proverb

I love to ask yoga students after class, "How are you?" The answer is considerably different than before class. Before class, the answers are usually information gathering, so I can know what problems or pains I can help with in the class. But after class — the problems and pains are usually gone. What remains is only a feeling — and what an amazing feeling it is!

A student recently said, "I feel so … (pause while searching for the word) … peaceful!? And I have lots of energy, too!" She was really surprised to feel these in combination. You already know how to push yourself and then mistake the exhaustion for peacefulness. You may experience peace only when you are completely drained. Later, when you have energy, you get back into the pushing mode — trying to do more of what you believe will make you feel good. It is called the "rat race."

The last article asked, "Who are you?" However, this question might be too esoteric to hold on to. It may be that the better question is, "How are you?" Moment to moment — how are you, really? You may be living on an emotional roller coaster. You can ride the ups and downs of constantly changing emotions for your whole life long — it is a "thrill-a-minute." How you are is in such flux that you cannot make plans or set goals, because what you think you want changes with each mood. There is a built in payoff — you are endlessly entertained by your own emotions, so you don't need to do much else with your life. You may have even perfected the ability to entertain everyone around you with your comedies and dramas!

Perhaps you handle it differently. How you are is not important because you are always the same — flat. I love those beautiful winter photographs on the front of Christmas cards, but the reality of living in numbing cold for months of every year interests me far less. Many people choose the emotional equivalent, numbing out by never feeling anything. The constancy and reliability provides ample opportunity to plan and accomplish things in life, but you never get to enjoy anything. What is the point of doing it if you cannot enjoy it?

You know the ever-present greeting, "Hi. How are you?" Nobody is really asking a question any more. No one is really answering. If you answer anything other than, "Fine," you create a problem. This is a hello, not an inquiry into your state, or (even worse) your health!

Let's find the yoga in the query, "How are you?" With everything in yoga, you turn it inside — ask yourself, "How am I?" This is very different than what you usually ask yourself. Without realizing it, you have been asking something entirely different. As a yoga teacher, I see this all the time. You bring more than your aches and pains with you when you come to class. You bring your mind-set, too. It shows up this way:

1. *"How do I look?"* I call this the high-heel syndrome. I remember when wearing the 3" heels was more important than the pain they caused. I was willing to go through the pain in order to get the "look." While they are in a pose, students sometimes even ask me, "How do I look?" I wish they were asking if they were in the angle that provides the maximum benefit, but they are actually asking if they are getting the "look."

2. *"How am I compared to other people?"* Some students look repeatedly around at the other people to see how they compare. One man told me that he did not want to come back because, "Everyone can touch their toes except me." He did not look at the results he got; he only looked at how he compared to everyone else!

3. *"How am I supposed to be?"* You already know how to live in the supposed-to's. You can be so busy analyzing how you should be doing it, you forget to notice how it actually feels.

These patterns do not show up only in yoga class — they are ways that you live your whole life! However, then you are not really *living* your life. You are living out what you think that other people think of you, or you are living out what you think you are supposed to be experiencing. Stop!

Use this little question, "How am I?" to guide you all the way to enlightenment. When the answer that arises inside is one of negativity or unhappiness, then you have lost the Self. When you feel only worry, fear or pain, you are *Velcro*-ed to things outside of you, hoping that they will somehow, someday make you happy. Peel off the *Velcro* and you will find happiness arising from inside. If you cannot peel off the *Velcro*, then at least do some yoga. Yoga will reliably change your feeling. You will always feel better after yoga. This is why I like to ask you *after class*, "How are you?"

But you do not have to wait until someone asks you. Check in with yourself, "How am I?" If the answer isn't good, remember — it is not the situation around you than needs to be changed. Change your internal environment. Use yoga to change the *Who* you are by monitoring the *How* you are, and it will take you all the way to the Self.

Reunion

September 2001

*"For him who sees him-Self in every self, in everything,
there is no longer left any perplexity, doubt, sorrow, fear."*
                                                        - The Upanishads

"Oneness is experienced from within. Oneness lives within."
                                                        - Iris Belhayes

CR

There is a priceless moment imbedded in the experience of greeting a loved one when they arrive at the airport. The *Vijnana Bhairava* describes this as one of the 112 shortcuts to bliss — reunion. When you suddenly see someone that you have been missing, a wonderful feeling arises inside. The reunion happens because two who had been separate now come together again. The Sanskrit word for this is "yoga." Yoga means union, which is technically a reunion. The two meeting at the airport were once together, were separated, and now they are meeting again. The meeting again is the greatest ecstasy of all. This yoga text says, "Seize upon the feeling! Forget the friend!" Because once the hellos and the hugs are over, you begin catching up on all the problems in each other's lives. Everything is downhill after that initial ecstasy of reunion.

The ancient sages describe this as being the principle underlying the creation of the universe. If the universe began with a "Big Bang" — what was there before the bang? There had to be something that went bang. What was it? Whatever name you ascribe to it, it is the source of the bang and the source of the universe. It continues to exist throughout the universe. It will absorb it all into itself again at the end of time. Yoga calls it Shiva and says that Shiva decided to "Bang!" The bang is a movement of Shiva, that is the energy that becomes the atoms, which then become everything that exists — by taking on a seeming separation. In other words, everything that exists (including you) is a form of Shiva, but does not know it is a form of Shiva. There is this seeming separation.

Yoga is the inner union. Yoga is the internal coming together, so you know again whom you have always been. You do not become someone else. You come home to who you have always been — the Self. Realization is exactly what it is named — you realize you have always been divine consciousness, but in an individualized form. "Oh, I am That. Of course."

These are not esoteric teachings that are distant from you and hard to reach. This is about how you feel and about who you are — every day. Some days, you just don't feel like yourself. There's a disconnect inside. Yoga is the plugging in – into the Source inside. One of the most frequent comments I hear is, "I feel like I have come home." The *Shavasana* at the end of class can take you to that deep inner dimension where you find yourself as the Self. It truly feels like coming home, on the inside. All the yoga practices are for the purpose of creating this inner experience. They are also really good for your body – but it is the inner dimension that is named by the word "yoga."

All this is why, on the outside, we love reunions. September is a traditional time of reunion. The summer is ended and you get back to your regular routine. It's wonderful to get back to the familiar — especially if you have been away from your yoga classes for a while. "Absence makes the heart grow fonder" can apply to yoga as well. That first class you take after you have been away feels so-o-o good. Fortunately, it just keeps getting better. Yoga is the only thing that I have ever found that keeps getting better, no matter how long I have been doing it.

Before I found yoga, I explored in many directions. Each foray showed me that it offered only limited happiness. I got to where I could figure this out in shorter and shorter time spans. I reached the point that I would start in a whole new direction and exhaust it within just six weeks. I began to wonder if I was going crazy! Then I found yoga. After six weeks, I was amazed to find that I was still interested. After six months, I could see that this was a deep well for me to drink from. One day, sitting on the side of my bed in the *ashram* (residential yoga center) in India, I realized I had been doing this for six years. At that point I thought, "Maybe this is a bottomless well." Now I know – It is.

Seeing Beyond the Illusion

October 2001

"Oh friend, where are you going? Where have you come from, and what are you supposed to do? You belong to the supreme Truth, but you have forgotten your origin. Now is the time to get back on the main road."

- Muktananda

"The height of all philosophy is to know thyself; and the end of this knowledge is to know God."

- Francis Quarles

In your head you have an idea of how the world works. It is not how the world works — it is your idea of how the world works. On September 11, 2001, that idea got shattered. Now you have to construct a new idea of how the world is. That idea will also be wrong, but you still must have an internal model.

This is the real change. The world-shaking events have done more than destroy airplanes, big buildings and thousands of lives. Beyond threatening your sense of personal or national safety, they have made your petty anxieties seem even pettier. Your most consuming ambitions and desires might seem insignificant now. The "big stuff" doesn't seem so big compared to the drama playing out on the world stage.

For thousands of years, yoga teachings have warned about getting caught up in the kaleidoscope of the world. You make a map in your mind about the way the world works. Then you place yourself in that map. It's like the big display board in the middle of the mall that has a red arrow saying, "You are here." Your sense of self is constructed within the landmarks of your mental map of the world. When the landmarks change, you don't know who you are anymore. That is what is happening now and it is happening to all of us, all at the same time. What is most amazing is that 260 million Americans, along with innumerable others, are all reconstructing their idea of the world at the same time.

The internal map you had been using was inaccurate. The world has really not changed. The world was not the way you thought it was. You have been living in an illusion of peace and safety, while the world has been in turmoil for decades. The landmarks have been there for a long time, but you may have been ignoring them. Multiple wars have been going on simultaneously throughout the last fifty years or more. Whole nations live under the threat of daily terrorism, with the corner grocery store being blown up moments after a person has walked out. Millions of people have been kidnapped in the middle of the night by their own government and never returned. Marauders and soldiers have been killing one another in the name of religion and/or race continuously throughout (probably) your whole lifetime. The only way you could have not known of this terrible daily risk was to work hard on blocking it out — to live in an illusion, more properly termed "delusion."

The Sanskrit term for illusion is *maya*. The One Reality hides itself within the world, which is an ever-changing phantasmagoria. Everything that exists is a unique manifestation of the One Reality — the formless appearing within form and activity. Thus, the world is real, but you must see beyond it to the unchanging ground of all Beingness. Most people become completely fascinated by the constant changes. They try to manipulate them in order to "win the game." This is the illusion, or the delusion — that the goal is found in the manipulating of the phenomena. The problem with *maya* is that you lose track of the greater Reality that pervades all of existence. When you see this Reality within yourself and within all forms, then you can be fully alive, fully human, and fully divine — simultaneously. Yoga describes this as seeing beyond the illusion.

These days, seeing beyond the illusion is the task at hand, in the profound ways and in a simpler way as well. The still-open wound that most of us are suffering from is the death of our illusion about how the world is. The everyday threat that so many have been living under worldwide is now personal and close up. You are staring death in the face. But this is not new. You always have been staring death in the face. Your risk of personal injury or death at the hand of a terrorist or madman has not increased by any percentage points at all. The chance that you will die in a car accident is much higher than dying from any political or personal act of violence. While you unconsciously plan on having decades more to do with as you please, you really don't know and you never have. This is the not the bad news — this is the good news.

Every day counts. Every breath matters. Every hello and every conversation is significant. If you wait until tomorrow or next year before you mend your broken bridges, you may not have the chance. If you deny the impulse of truth arising within you, you may not have another opportunity to follow up on it. To look death in the face is to find life.

It is so tempting to try to patch your old worldview back together. If you succeed with the spit and baling wire, something else will have to happen to blow it apart. Recognize the reality of the world. See past the illusion. The world is a mixture of pleasant and painful things. Experience it and look past it. Live in the world and look beyond it. Relationships are a mixture; your job is a mixture; your life has its tides — high and low. Admit it and find something more. Discover the meaning of life inside yourself. Delve inside to find the source of the light that shines through your eyes. Live from the Source. Or at least do what you need to do in order to reconnect with that source inside — do more yoga!

Bittersweet

November 2001

*"Pain is a blessing in disguise. Pain is an eye-opener.
Pain is your silent teacher. Pain will turn your mind toward God."*

- Sivananda

*"God whispers to us in our pleasures, speaks in our conscience, but
shouts in our pains: it is a megaphone to rouse the deaf world."*

- C. S. Lewis

CR

The holiday season is upon us. At the end of every year, we turn to celebrations of gratitude, light and God's grace, even in the echo of recent tragedies and in the midst of continuing turmoil. Can we laugh and feast when so many are still suffering? How can we celebrate when so many have died?

A celestial being brought together Confucius, Buddha and Shankaracharya for a taste test. He served a clear liquid containing the essence of the world to each in turn. Buddha took a sip, puckered up and frowned. He said, "This cup is bitter. All life is suffering. The world is full of pain." Confucius sipped from the same cup and said, "How sweet this tastes! The world is an amazing interplay of dynamics that play out through human relationships and in society. Life is wonderful." Then it was the yogi's turn. Shankaracharya sipped and smiled, saying, "You are both right. The world is full of pain and it is wonderful. This cup is bittersweet — the best of all tastes!"

Yoga recognizes both light and shadow as manifestations of the one Reality. Neither one is inherently better than the other. We live in what yoga calls the pairs of opposites: pleasure-pain, happy-sad, good-bad, right-wrong, etc. Recognize your own tendency to bounce back and forth between the pairs of opposites. While the pairs are real, they are not the whole story. You must look deeper and discover the source within yourself.

If you take on the pain of others, you fall into what I call the "Bodhisattva Trap." Some sects of Buddhism give initiation only after you have taken the bodhisattva vow: that you will not allow yourself to become enlightened until everyone in the world is there. It is a deeply compassionate vow. The most well known of those who have taken it is the Dalai Lama, who takes birth again and again to help shepherd us into our own divinity.

This vow is often misunderstood. To be compassionate does not mean you should be in pain. Helping others does not depend on you feeling their pain. That is the trap that many got caught in after September 11, 2001. "Since others are in pain, I must be in pain, too." No. You can and you must be in a better state than the ones you want to help. You must be in an expanded and exalted inner state in order to help others reach their own.

To avoid the Bodhisattva Trap, it is easy to go too far the other way. The "Hedonist Trap" awaits. Many are now falling into this one, "Forget others' pain by indulging in my desires." You can distract yourself from your own pain as well as from seeing and knowing what is going on in the world. You can do yoga to forget that so many were killed, especially if you didn't know any of them personally. It is easy to ignore that the American military has moved into high gear on the other side of the globe. This is a way of being unconsciousness in a very sophisticated form.

Find the middle road. Avoid both the Bodhisattva Trap and the Hedonist Trap. In the midst of death, celebrate life. In the midst of pain, give thanks for your blessings. In the midst of war, gather together for a reunion with your loved ones, for a few hours or a few days. It makes it all more precious, somehow. Life is bittersweet. It always has been. Know and live it all in fullness, as living yoga.

Of all the chocolates, the bittersweet is the best. Baker's chocolate is too bitter to eat. Milk chocolate is sometimes sappy-sweet. You eat piece after piece but you're never satisfied. One small piece of bittersweet chocolate gives a multi-layered satisfaction that lasts for a long time. May your holidays be truly holy-days.

PART III

❦

Inside Out

Rama's Training as a Teacher

Richard Hittelman captivated me every time I caught his yoga show on television, which wasn't often. As a full-time mother of three small children, I would tune in once every week or two. I actually did very few of the poses he led. Instead I "soaked up the vibe" without understanding what was so captivating to me. Four or five years later, I took an introductory meditation class at the local college. My meditations at home catapulted me into amazing inner experiences and gave me many questions. The meditation teacher referred me to someone else who "might be able to answer me." So I visited a free meditation program offered by this second teacher. This weekly program was complete with chanting in Sanskrit and big pictures of an Indian *Guru* on the walls. I thought it was very strange, especially since I "fell asleep" during the meditation. A few weeks later, I had a spontaneous experience of energy surging up my spine - it was ecstatic! I felt drawn to return to the meditation center even though I had not been meditating when the energy opened up inside.

This pivotal experience became a daily event as I sat for an hour of meditation in the early morning before my children awoke. As soon as I would settle into a quiet seated position, the *Kundalini* energy began to move up my spine. It moved me into spontaneous *asanas* (yoga poses). This rekindled my interest in *hatha yoga*, the practice of the *asanas*, so I began taking yoga classes. In the middle of practicing a pose, *Kundalini* would take over and move me further than I would ever have dreamed I could go, sometimes even further than I might have wanted to go! Yet something more than extreme poses was blossoming inside. My mental capacity expanded, along with an incredible clarity that banished doubt and fear. My newfound ability to love my children while providing the needed discipline and guidance was something I had never imagined possible. My energy level was inexhaustible, which was truly needed as I was now a single mother working full time.

Within a few months, I shared with my yoga (*asana*) teacher that I was interested in teaching. I asked her what Teacher Training program she would recommend. She said, "You already know enough. You can teach now." I continued to study with her while I advertised and began teaching a course in my living room. After the third class I taught, a student asked me about a pain in her knee. I did not know the answer. I recognized again that I needed more training. I enrolled with a second local teacher, who had been appointed to train teachers by her *Guru*. Midway through that training, I was swept on a wave of grace all the way to India, where I met my *Guru* in person for the first time. Astounding experiences and understandings opened daily for those three weeks, as *Kundalini* continued to dance through my spine.

When I returned, I completed the local teacher training course and was certified as a hatha yoga teacher. However, the discrepancy between my inner and outer experiences was even greater than before. When *Kundalini* moved me through *asanas*, my spine opened to a supple vitality, which became more and more subtle and profound. It was the experience of diving deep within to climb up the spine, the inner conduit to God. But when I did the poses as I had been trained by both of my *asana* teachers, my body stretched on the outside while the core became tight and compressed. At the end of a class, I felt good - but it was a physical high, not a "Consciousness" high. I concluded that there was something wrong with me and that I just needed more training.

I decided to pursue that training under the guidance of my *Guru*, and moved into the *ashram* (residential yoga center) with my children. The daily program of yoga practices emphasized meditation and chanting along with the daily work it takes to keep *ashram* activities going. The work was one of the key practices, called *seva* (selfless service). It easily became a living yoga, as Krishna describes in the <u>Bhagavadgita</u>. *Sadhana* (spiritual practice) did not mean the hour each day that we did our meditation or other practices, but expanded to mean life itself - life lived as a continuing yoga. Amazingly, the *asanas* were optional!

Kundalini still moved me through *asanas* every time I sat to meditate. I enrolled in the optional yoga classes to continue my training — at 5 a.m. daily. In India I was certified as a hatha yoga teacher, advanced hatha yoga teacher, *pranayama* (breathing) teacher, and meditation teacher. I was trained in the texts and, most importantly, steeped in the blessing of a Master who lived in the state that the texts promise to all.

After almost seven years of studying and living in that environment, I returned to California. I set up housekeeping in the suburbs, bought a station wagon and began chauffeuring my children to soccer games and other activities. I got a job and started teaching a couple of evening yoga classes in my home. I discovered that the yoga landscape in California had changed in the years I was gone. I was told, "If you do not teach strenuous yoga, you are not teaching yoga." Wow! So, I started taking strenuous yoga classes. But my body and soul already knew an experience that this approach did not match. Even the *asana* training I had in India seemed like "cookie-cutter yoga" to me. My body could do the poses — as though I were "posing" for a camera but what happened inside was not what I knew as "yoga." Again, I thought it was probably just something wrong with me. So I continued taking strenuous yoga classes.

With hindsight, now I see that I learned important principles from each of the four styles I had studied: from my first teacher, I learned about the love of God; from that first Teacher Training, I learned to practice a few key poses with consistency and focus; from my classical training in India, I learned rigorous discipline; from strenuous yoga, I learned about precision and props.

Life continued to roll me along with a few years in the suburbs and a few more years in the *ashram*, until it landed me in San Diego. I started teaching yoga. But I could see that all my techniques did not offer the students the inner opening that I knew was available. Everything I had learned through twelve years of training actually seemed to get in the way for them. One Saturday morning, as I was talking the class through *Pawanmuktasana* (Alternate Leg Pose), I simply told them to move their knee to a different angle. All four styles I was trained in said this was the WRONG ANGLE! I actually considered for a moment that I might get struck by lightening for doing it wrong. Still, I somehow knew it would reach through the outer layers of the body to open deep into the core — to open the spine from the tailbone first, just as *Kundalini* had been doing for me through all these years.

Students came to me at the end of class, excitedly asking, "What was that!?" They felt something open up in their body. More importantly, they found a deeper level of inner absorption in the closing *Shavasana*. Week by week, I began to sneak a few more of these forbidden angles into each class, until I was teaching only these angles that reliably opened the spine. Within two years, students were interested in becoming teachers of this approach. I went to India and got my *Guru's* blessing to begin training teachers. I referred to it still by the generic "hatha yoga."

Only after a Sanskrit teacher visited my class did I begin to consider giving it a name. After the class, he told me that he traveled and taught in major yoga schools and *ashrams* all over the U.S., and that this was different from anything else being taught. I was not surprised because I had needed years to unlearn all the things I had diligently learned over the prior years. Students' questions had forced me to express my non-verbal knowing in descriptions that they could follow in their own inner experience, both of the body and of that greater Reality within. He warned me that I must name this approach, or they would call it "Rama Yoga." That could never be acceptable to me, because this was a gift of grace I had received, not something I had created.

I asked for his help. With his help, I selected *svaroopa* as the best name, one that points at both the practice and the goal.

> "*Sva*" means Self, the one Reality at the foundation of all existence (including your own)
> "*roopa*" means form, shape, substance.

> "*Svaroopa*" is the form of the Self, the essence of Consciousness-Itself, the Bliss of Your Own Being.

> *Svaroopa* is also a play on words, because it is a description of what we do, using *roopa* (your form = your body) to reach *sva* (the Self within).

We use the *asanas* as tools to open your spine, which opens interior access to *svaroopa*, the Bliss of your own Being. We develop through athletic poses as the intermediate level. The advanced level of our practice is "Bliss Yoga," where we use subtle and sophisticated techniques to open through your body to the deeper levels of being. Again, I trekked to my *Guru* for permission and blessing to found Master Yoga Foundation. Again, I received, as always, more than I ever hoped for. If the way I work with the body can be of service, then my work is my *sadhana*, along with the rest of my life. Thank you for the opportunity to serve you.

I Am Not A Sinner

Vision Magazine, December 1996

"I have a problem with sin," I explained to my minister about why I had requested the meeting. "I do not believe myself to be a sinner. I never have." Then I added, "Maybe it is a sin to believe that I'm not a sinner, but deep down inside I just do not feel like a sinner. I have even done some wrong things in my life. But something inside says I am not a sinner. The Church keeps telling me I am. I cannot continue to come to Church if I have to believe I am a sinner. Am I a sinner?"

I had been in one or another flavor of Christianity all of my adult life. My parents (one Jewish, one Protestant) had told me to choose my own religion. My girlfriend took me with her to her church as a teenager. I had taken two years of Catechism classes and was baptized and confirmed. I had my children baptized when they were born, then volunteered in the Church nursery and taught in the Sunday School. I even tried the Ladies Auxiliary, but just could not fit in with all the blue-haired ladies talking about their quilts and playing bridge. Every Sunday, when I stood to "confess my sins before God-the-Almighty-Father," it was a lie. I was going through the motions of a ritual that was totally meaningless to me. I figured that either I was so bad off that I did not even know I was a sinner, or that the Church was wrong.

Dr. Smith was a new minister, actually an interim minister. Our regular guy was in Europe for the summer. Dr. Smith was the summer fill-in. He still had one more year to go in the seminary. He was willing to start his answer with, "I do not know."

I went on and described the yoga books I had been reading. "Yoga tells me I am Divine Consciousness. This feels true to me. These books say that I am a perfect manifestation of Divine Consciousness, but that I do not know it. All I have to do is realize the Truth that already dwells inside. Christianity tells me I'm a sinner and that I need someone else to redeem me before God. I cannot stay in the Church if that's what I am supposed to believe."

He said, "Let us look up the word 'sin.'" He began to pull books off the shelves. In each one he checked the index for sin. Every book had many entries, but none of them offered a definition. After six or seven books, he drew down a thick encyclopedia and found the entry. The definition ran several pages long and began with, "sin: separation from God."

In triumph I shouted, "Yes! That I have got!" I knew I felt separate from God. I had wanted all my life to end that agonizing separation. The yoga philosophy I had been studying had helped me to clarify my understanding of this unnamed feeling I suffered from for so long. If the Church wanted to call that feeling of separation by the name "sin," it was okay with me. I said, "I have sin, but I am not a sinner."

We talked for another hour or so. He ended with asking me to give the sermon on the next Sunday. My parents came. I quoted the Bible, the _Upanishads_ and the _Gurus_ with whom I had been studying. I described how I was inspired by the teachings of yoga, instead of being downtrodden by the doctrine that I am a sinner. I invited everyone to think differently of himself or herself. I stood with the minister at the door as the congregation hugged and thanked me as they left. I felt validated and confirmed. It was a new type of confirmation: a confirmation in the faith, but a _different faith_ than I had before.

I never went back. The support of that open-hearted, open-minded minister along with the love and enthusiasm of the others in the church gave me the freedom to fly. It is as though I had always had wings but I would never have known it. Yoga told me I had wings, and these wonderful people gave me their blessing to learn to fly.

I went to Dr. Smith's ordination ceremony a year later. I had been certified as a yoga teacher and taken my first trip to India to meet my _Guru_. He had graduated from the seminary and found a Church to serve. The seminary could not ordain him. Only the congregation could. I sang at his ceremony and thanked him for giving me the freedom to use my wings. And I realized I had been ordained by my own congregation the year before. I felt (though I did not dare say out loud), "I am done with Christianity."

I studiously avoided all Christian holidays for the next fifteen years, even making sure I was out of the country almost every Christmas. I studied yoga philosophy. I chanted to Shiva, to Krishna and to the _Guru_ three times a day for 3,000 days. I found the basic principles were expressed in a way that resonated so deep inside me that I can only call it "Truth." Then I became interested in the new books being published on Christianity. I discovered they were talking about the same thing that had driven me to my minister ten years earlier. I found the connections between the two philosophies: What Christianity calls "original sin" is termed in yoga as "delusion." "Holy Spirit" is "grace." "Redemption" is "rediscovery." The two came together for me in my heart. My own roots from growing up with both Judaism and Christianity became a treasured part of my path in yoga.

Still, I was really shocked when Jesus showed up one day. While I was giving a private yoga session, my client began to cry some quiet sweet tears. She said that Jesus had come. He gave her a blessing and a kiss on her forehead. I was fine with that, because I respected her beliefs. But when she had gone and I was straightening up the room, suddenly I felt His presence. I did not see Him, but He was there. I was amazed to discover that I was angry! I began yelling at Him on the inside, "What are *you* doing here! I want nothing to do with you and your cross. You can keep it! I want nothing to do with it!" He stayed.

Narada says in the *Bhakti Sutras* that there are many different ways you can be in relationship with God. You can love Him as a father, brother, sister, lover or friend. You can love Him as a child, which is why so many people love to celebrate Christmas. Narada goes on to say that you should direct every emotion to God. In the *Mahabharata*, Duryodhana causes the destruction of his own race. Yet he ends up going to heaven because when he was sad, he cried out to God. When he was angry, he shook his fist at God and cursed Him. I took Narada literally.

The second day Jesus continued to hang around with me. I continued to rant and rave, all on the inside. The third day I realized I had been carrying His cross, even though I thought I had left Christianity. One of my shoulders was even mounded up higher than the other, like I had been dragging that heavy stick of wood around with me as I traveled the world in my studies and my work. I quietly gave Him back His cross. My shoulder relaxed down and quit hurting. In His quiet presence I came to understand that He had never wanted me to carry that cross. That is why He had given His life, so I would not have to. Somewhere through the centuries, the message had gotten garbled, so I had labored in pain.

Then I became angry with Him for what was taught in His name. After all, it was His church, so was He not in charge? He stayed quietly with me, until I saw that He could not make it go any differently. If He changed what we would do, it would deny us our free will. I saw the tremendous love that motivated His actions, both in His life and in the centuries since then.

He stayed with me for another day or so. I told Him that I could not be part of His church again. Now though, I accepted His support and His love. Only then did He leave. But He's not really gone. If my mind wanders even the slightest bit in that direction, I feel His presence as a comfort and support. I see His eyes watching me. I ask for His help when I am working with those who have a meaningful relationship with Him. I think of Him as a buddy, a friend. But I don't think of Him as my Savior, because I don't need saving. I am not a sinner.

Hatha Yoga is a Spiritual Path

Vision Magazine, September 1995

As it is taught in modern America, hatha yoga, most often called simply "yoga," is incredibly effective as exercise. It is a powerful tool for maintaining health, strength and youth. Most Americans are interested in being strong and healthy, and especially interested in staying young or young looking. Thus, media attention focuses on the incredible physical benefits of yoga, all of which are true. Yoga relieves back pain, panic attacks, headaches, allergies, PMS, anxiety, arthritis, constipation, high blood pressure, stress, and more.

However, this understanding of yoga is very limiting. It is like going to a gourmet restaurant and ordering potato chips and soda. Though you become more fit and flexible when you practice yoga; that is not all you get. You will also enjoy a better attitude, more mental clarity, better ability to focus, and greater happiness. You will live your life against a background of inner tranquility that guides and supports you in every situation. And you will have access to a deeper and more profound level of your own Being.

Yoga is actually an ancient mystical tradition, which teaches the mysteries of life. It opens the doorway to your inner essence of Truth, Light, Joy and Love. Once you tap into this infinite source, your whole life is transformed. You shine with inner love and joy that you feel and know with your whole being. It fills your body, mind, heart and soul. You understand the meaning of life and you live it with every breath. You see the light of divine consciousness in every person and every situation. Your life becomes the vehicle through which grace and blessings flow.

So, the question arises, "You get all of that from stretching?" The answer is "Yes and No." Yoga is not just stretching, nor is it merely another form of exercise. Yoga is a highly sophisticated means of working with your body to accomplish a higher purpose. It is similar to the difference you experience between jogging for your health and jogging for world hunger. Yoga exercises clear and open your body so that you can hold the ecstatic states of enlightenment.

The ancient tradition of yoga includes yoga poses (*asana*), breathing methods (*pranayama*) and energy seals (*mudra*). It also offers guidelines for daily living (*yamas* and *niyamas*) and focusing practices (*dharana*). You can progress to mastery of the energies of your senses (*pratyahara*), meditation (*dhyana*), absorption into your own inner ecstasy (*samadhi*), and even beyond that to enlightenment. All of these practices include a range from the very easy to the more subtle and profound.

One of the simplest and most effective things yoga teaches is to learn how to sigh. Right after a thorough, heart-felt sigh, there is an incredible feeling of stillness. This stillness transcends the world of space and time. It gives you an immediate taste of your own inner potential. Yoga is the science of maximizing that potential.

Yoga also offers study of the ancient texts that describes the nature of your own Being. It includes the science of sound, the inspiration we get from enlightened Masters of all traditions, and the opening of your heart to the divine presence that is always both within and outside.

In *Svaroopa Yoga*, we work with the body for your specific purpose of having this inner experience. Everything we do, from the easiest to the most challenging, is for the higher purpose that is yoga itself. Yoga philosophy is embedded in everything we teach, just as joy should be embedded in every moment of your life and in every part of your body. Only then will you unlock the mystery of the meaning of life.

Yoga in Today's World

adapted from "Yoga and Ayurveda in the Material World"

Inside Ayurveda Magazine, Spring/Summer 1999

Thirty years ago, as a stay-at-home mom with three kids, I bought two show-quality Dalmatians to begin breeding and selling puppies. To raise their value, we needed show ribbons, so I learned to train dogs for both conformance and obedience. I also discovered that popularity is the worst thing that can happen to a breed. Backyard breeders begin producing puppies without selectivity, so breed quality goes downhill.

I sometimes question if the same thing is happening to yoga in America. A survey by IDEA Health & Fitness, Inc. (*IDEA Fitness Manager, October 1998*) shows that 53 percent of all U.S. athletic clubs now offer yoga. Many club members want a yoga workout as part of their cross-training regimen. But they may never hear from their yoga teacher that:

- yoga is the science of consciousness,
- the asanas (poses, stretches, exercises) are a small part of yoga's incredible technology
- yoga's true purpose is to cultivate a deepening experience of your own eternal boundless essence as Consciousness-Itself.

Though I am thrilled that there are now 20 million Americans practicing yoga, I am concerned that too many are coming with the intention of creating eternal youth and beauty, or hoping that yoga will heal the injuries or illnesses that modern medicine cannot cure. I would love to be able to offer every yoga student the healing they seek, but some physical conditions may not improve. Yet yoga offers true healing, which is the rediscovery of your own essence as Consciousness-Itself.

Hatha Yoga techniques are most effective when they open the student to the awareness of Consciousness, through clearing away the tensions in the body. Consciousness is the most powerful healing agent of all. So we get miracle stories and showy images, which the media loves, because it helps them sell their publication. But when do the gymnastics take over and distort people's understanding of yoga? Some yoga poses photograph well, while meditation does not.

The major schools that train yoga teachers have created the national Yoga Alliance, as trailblazers in setting standards for yoga teachers. A teacher with training in physical techniques only does not qualify as a Registered Yoga Teacher (R.Y.T.). A teacher must have training in anatomy and supervised teaching experience, along with courses in yoga philosophy and meditation. As the first President of Yoga Alliance, I feel strongly about bringing Consciousness back into yoga. I pray that all yogis remember the goal — to know your own Divinity. Do more yoga.

Sacred Body

Vision Magazine, January 1996

Your body does not exist. What appears to be flesh and bones is not physical matter at all. It is a collection of atoms swirling around in empty space. Vedanta says that everything is unreal, it is all illusion. Buddhism says that all life is suffering. This might be a valid description of your life, if you obsess on the illusion as though it were Reality. But yoga says something completely different. Yoga says that all life is sacred, including your body.

To understand the sacredness of your body, you need only consider of what it is made. Your physical body is made of atoms. The atoms are not themselves solid matter, but are made of subatomic particles. The subatomic particles are also not really particles. They are all tiny bits of contracted energy moving at preposterous speeds in a vast amount of empty space. The energy that makes up your body is the same as the energy that manifests as the plants, the ocean, the moon and the stars. This energy swirls in differing patterns, which determine what the physical object will be. This energy dances in these intricate patterns on a background of unmoving empty space the physicists now tell us is not really empty. It is full of something, but they do not know what the "something" is.

Where did the energy come from? The physicists cannot yet answer this. They begin to sound like the poets and mystics when they speculate on the answer. It does not matter if they ever give us an answer, because the question is itself important. Consider it for yourself. When you begin to consider your body as consisting of energy dancing in complex patterns in space, your experience of your body and your experience of who you are changes. You begin to know the meaning of the word, "sacred." The knowing of this cannot be described in words. Your body is a sacred place.

For ten years I traveled all over the world, spending extended periods of time in many different countries and cultures. In retrospect I realize that what I had been doing was visiting sacred places. I lit candles in medieval cathedrals, bowed my head in Hindu temples, lit incense in Chinese and Japanese temples, sat in Buddhist monasteries, and stood in the back of Islamic mosques. In Granada, Spain, I visited synagogues that had been desecrated by the government when they expelled the Jews in the 1400's. The buildings were then converted to churches and are now standing empty. Standing inside I could tell that they are still sacred.

I climbed mountains and watched oceans, rivers and waterfalls. I attended fire ceremonies and sweat lodges. Mosques were the hardest for me to comprehend. It was in Malaysia that I experienced, finally, the sacredness of Islam. Then, somehow the pilgrimages were complete. I knew, in a way that words cannot describe, that every religion is valid and that every place is sacred. The spot where you now stand is sacred ground. There is not anywhere that isn't sacred. *Na shivam vidyate kvachit* – there is nowhere that God is not. In a movie, John Denver stood dripping wet in a newspaper office after God (played by George Burns) had made it rain inside the car. "But you do not understand!" he shouted to the reporter. "This is holy water! God made it!" The newspaperman was not impressed. Where is there water that God did not make?

Many years ago a New York City rabbi was great friends with an Indian *Guru*. The rabbi would visit for long philosophical discussions with the Indian holy man. After many months of weekly visits, the rabbi brought up a topic that had been bothering him for some time. "You have many beautiful statues in your garden, *Swami*. But your statue of Moses is against the rules of my religion, as God forbids the making of images." The *Swami* replied with a question, "Does your God exist in the heavens?" "Yes," said the rabbi. "Does your God exist in the stars?" "Yes, he does." "Does your God exist in the earth and the water and the streams?" "Oh, yes," said the rabbi. "Does your God exist in the plants and flowers?" "Yes, my God exists everywhere," said the rabbi. "Then what makes you think He does not exist inside the statue, too?" The rabbi paused. He finally replied, "I will have to think about that."

What makes you think God does not exist inside yourself. Does that presence stop at the outside of your skin? Take a breath. Pause. Consider again: Of what substance are you made? A Sufi saint once said that you can tear down a church, you can break apart a synagogue or temple, you can burn down a mosque, but you must never break a human heart, for that is where God resides.

The spot where you now stand is sacred ground. And you, the one standing on it, are also sacred ground. It is what you do with the ground that makes it a holy place or not. With an empty field you can build a temple, a park, a hospital, a nightclub or a cemetery. Regardless of what you build, the ground

214

itself does not change. The difference is only a decision. The same is true with your body. Your body is like the vacant field. You can do with it whatever you decide.

Your body usually lags two or more years behind your mind. In other words if you quit smoking, your body will be healing the effects of your previous habit for two years or longer. If you change your eating habits, your body will take some time to go through a process of becoming healthier. Still, it is really about your mind, because first there must be a decision to make the changes.

Even more powerfully, yoga says you digest your thoughts. You can eat all the "right" foods, but if you continue a steady diet of negative or fearful thoughts, you will be sick. You must begin to see the sacred in everyone and in every-thing. This is what it truly means to change your thoughts. When someone cuts you off on the freeway, offer them that piece of the road with generosity. I learned this from a driver on the freeway. He had been changing lanes furiously and was tailgating me so I blocked him. When he finally got by me, he rolled down his window and shouted "My dog was hit by a car, and I am trying to get him to the vet." Give that spot on the road to the frantic driver, thinking that maybe he or she needs it more than you do. Or maybe they only think they need it, so give them your compassion, too.

You need some retraining. Your training in life has been programming in negativity, fear, need and greed. This has created your need for relentless activity. This perpetual activity masks the underlying insecurities that come from your not knowing the sacred in yourself. You may need help with your retraining. Take trainings, workshops or study with someone who currently knows more about it than you do.

In the meantime, keep an eye out for the sacred. It can be found in so many moments of your day. Use the red traffic signals as a reminder to slow down. Take a breath and look around. Maybe you will see a flower, or notice the color of the sky. When you're stuck in line at the sandwich counter or photocopier, take it as a reminder from God to see this place as a sacred place. Look at everyone there as being energy. Find the sacred even in a person you don't like. Find the sacred in yourself.

The spot where you now stand is sacred ground. You, standing on it, and your body, with which you stand, are also sacred. *Na shivam vidyate kvachit* — there is nowhere that God is not. There is nothing that is not divine. You are a manifestation of God. See what it is like to live in a world where everything is sacred and God is not far away. Look inside yourself, or look into the light shining through the eyes of another person, and you will see that God is close to you. The divine is never far away. Then see what kind of decisions you make. How will you decide to use your mind — to profane the sacred or to honor it and make it shine? What kind of life do you want to live? It is only a decision away. The spot where you now stand is sacred ground.

The Yoga of Earth
Vision Magazine, April 1994

The Old Testament gives a description of God shaping man out of earth, breathing "into his nostrils the breath of life" (Genesis 2.7). Yoga names your physical body "*anna-maya-kosha*," the level of individual consciousness that is created and sustained by food (*anna*) which comes from the earth. You are referred to as the embodied soul. Your body is honored as a temple, like a holy place that one would visit to experience a profound connection with the divine. The physical practices of yoga enable you to experience your body as the temple of Consciousness-Itself.

Everything that exists is comprised of the five primary elements, according to the ancient sages. The element of earth (*prithivee*) includes the ground on which you stand, the minerals suspended in water, and the solids floating in air. Water (*ap*) is found in lakes and streams, as well as the clouds and the humidity of air. Fire (*agni*) has been tamed to offer us fuel for heating and cooking, while it includes the untamed fires that arise from the molten core of the center of the earth. Air (*vaata*) is what we breathe, the atmosphere surrounding the planet and suffusing the sunlight to give us the beautiful colors at the beginning and end of the day. Space (*aakkasha*) is the background upon which all this manifests, the seemingly empty space through which the atoms swirl.

These five elements combine to form your body in an individualized way that is a perfect expression of your uniqueness. Earth gives your body its form and shape. Water provides the life-giving fluids inside, as well as the capacity to move. Fire is your digestive system, the warmth of your body and the warmth of your heart. Air is your breath and is the primary quality of your mind. Space is the hollow space inside your organs.

Your bones are the fullest expression of the element of earth in your body. They are made of minerals, like stones. Their solidity and density provide support for your body. Bones get strong when you use them. They weaken if you do not. Unfortunately, most people do not actually use their bones for support. Most people hold themselves up with their muscles, instead of leaning into their bones. To be centered and grounded you must stand in the bones of your feet, or sit on the "sit-bones" at the base of your buttocks. Lean into your bones. Relax into your bones. Let them hold you up.

Your first *chakra* (the primary energy center at the tip of your tailbone) houses the principle of earth. It is here that you learn to make it in the world, whether it is bare survival or great abundance. At this level you have the opportunity to become free from fear. You can master the physical plane and go on to the other issues of life: relationship, work, self-expression, insight and service. When this *chakra* is opened and balanced, your life falls together instead of falling apart. You become supremely glad to be alive and possess great health and vitality. You enjoy your own body without obsessing on it.

Smell comes from the element of earth. A handful of earth has a scent. Experienced farmers sniff the earth to gauge its properties. You may have experienced how a sudden whiff of a scent from your past can thrust you into memory. The experience can be so vivid that you are reliving it rather than simply remembering it. A highly sensitive nose can be an indication of extra sensory perception. A diminished sense of smell may indicate suppression of emotions or memories that make you feel threatened.

The element of earth is also associated with excretion. In many countries, human waste is an essential part of agriculture. Rather than polluting rivers or oceans, this form of earth is returned to the earth. Your own ancestors fertilized their farms in this way. But excretion is more than merely physical. Excretion is the ability to let go. This is easy if your sense of personal survival or safety is not dependent on the externals. But if your first *chakra* is still out of balance, you may find that letting go is not so easy.

Many yoga practices work specifically on this. This includes *yoga* poses and other practices that give you a strong sense of self, through finding your own Source in the inner realms. The development of your own power and potential through these *yoga* practices is both immediate and long term. Consult with your *yoga* teacher for advice on your specific needs, both for physical poses and for exposing the inner realms of consciousness.

There are some fun and easy things you can do to stimulate and balance the element of earth in your body. Sit on the floor. Take off your shoes and walk barefoot. Sidewalks are good, for they are made of stone. Walking in dirt or mud is even better, and it is fun. Dig in the dirt, either to plant a garden or to make a few mud pies. Maybe you would rather build a sand castle. Sit in the sand without a blanket or chair underneath you. Visualize your bones and lean into them. Find a small stone and carry it in your pocket or purse. Handle it frequently, but do not get too attached to it. Give it back to the earth and borrow another. Pick up a handful of earth and smell it. Pour the first few drops of your glass of water on the earth as an offering, like the Vikings of old. Remind yourself to live in your body, not just in your head. You will like it.

Clean Up Your Inner Act
Vision Magazine, January 1994

The environment is an external manifestation of the inner environment. The pollution we experience in the world is coming from inside ourselves. Air pollution is a manifestation of our polluted thoughts, the unceasing stream of inner negativity and anxiety. Water pollution is a reflection of our polluted relationships, the flow of garbage we project outward onto those closest to us. Toxic waste in the earth is the outward expression of what we have stuffed into our unconscious, which then shows up in our physical pains and diseases. We are cutting down our forests because we have cut ourselves off from our source. We are strip mining the earth and over fishing the oceans because we are so hungry to find the answers. But we are looking in the wrong place.

Ya drishti sa srishtihi. What you see outside of you arises from within. Sanskrit offers answers to the timeless questions. The words of the ancient yogis are alive, as relevant today as when they were first written. Their prescription for outer improvement is to change your inner environment.

The sages explain how to affect this inner and outer transformation. We are all aware of some ways to effect personal change, like doing yoga. But when you take your inner attitude into the poses with you (and how do you avoid that?), then all you have is a sophisticated form of exercise. You can try meditation, but can you really use the mind to go beyond the mind? You can use psychic or metaphysical techniques, but you're still looking outside yourself for the answers that are truly within. Even psychology seems to have forgotten "psyche," the soul.

The power of the Sanskrit language takes you to the inner experience, which is beyond the subtle and subversive mind chatter that taints everything you see and understand. You can affirm to yourself in any language that your inner being is eternal, pure and perfect. Yet, when you listen to or you chant in Sanskrit, you experience that eternal purity and perfection that you are. It goes beyond being a theory, and becomes a reality. Sanskrit was designed to create this inner experience. It arose out of the Inner Truth and it takes you back home into it again.

As described by Vyaas Houston, founder of the American Sanskrit Institute, this "… language of the human spirit seems to be in every way the perfect instrument for bringing about healing on many levels. Its great power lies in bringing body, mind and spirit into harmonic alignment. Physically, its resonating power promotes healing. Mentally, it awakens the natural brightness, agility and order of the mind. Spiritually, it facilitates an expansion of awareness, tranquility, and bliss."

This inner experience completely changes the way you deal with the world, and the kind of world you co-create. Relationships, work, play and the environment all benefit from your inner inspiration, from your clarity and from the love you are now free to express. Such outer transformation will not occur without the inner transformation. Your efforts to serve the world will be a thousand times more effective with this inner clarity and peace.

Make Your Life Spiritual
Vision Magazine, September 2001

I sat next to a world famous violinist who had fascinating stories to tell. The eighteen hours of flight, traveling to India, is an amazingly intimate setting; sharing that small space for such a long time. He had studied at Juilliard and with the greatest violin masters all over Europe. He traveled to perform as a soloist with major symphonies throughout the world. Now, at the top of his profession, he was going to study an entirely different method with an Indian violin master. He spoke reverentially of this great teacher, "He will start me at the beginning all over again."

My heart was opened by his words, because it was exactly what my own teacher had done, though it was in a different field of endeavor. My *Guru* stripped me of all that I thought I was. Then, he pieced me back together again in a whole new way. He gave me my Self. It was not easy, and it was not quick. After more than twenty-five years, it is still going on. However, I cannot describe what the current stages are because I do not understand the stages I have not passed through. All I can say is, "Study with a Master."

Too many seekers are reading books by unenlightened beings, asking other seekers for guidance and stumbling around in their own minds and emotions. Too many teachers are trying to lead you where they have not gone. It is amazingly easy to find a genuine Master to study with — they even come to San Diego! Go *Guru*-shopping. I highly recommend it. It is even more fun than other kinds of shopping. Meet several enlightened beings. One will touch your heart in a special way. You'll never look back at how life used to be.

If you cannot find an enlightened being to study with, at least get your spiritual teachings from someone who has decades of practice under a Master. If someone is teaching something that they recently learned, or (worse) that they made up — run the other way! Do not let someone else experiment with your spiritual development. It is the spiritual equivalent of a phenomenon best named by Hollywood, "Dumb and Dumber."

If you cannot find a spiritual teacher who has been doing their practices for a long time, then begin with simple and safe spiritual practices. You have a number of choices:

1. Go to church. Look for your fulfillment in the ceremony, not in the minister or in the social scene.
2. Repeat a mantra — one from your own tradition or religion is best. Repeat it all the time!
3. Meditate and/or pray daily.
4. Do yoga, tai chi, African drumming, Sufi dancing or any other spiritual practice for the body — with the emphasis on your inner experience, instead of the perfection of the body or on the social connections. Pick only one. Do it daily.
5. Make social connections with others who share your practice. Though you do your practice for the inner effects, you need the support of like-minded people to keep you on track. Still, they are not your Master. They are your traveling companions along the path.
6. Give of yourself. Give your time and money to organizations you believe in. Volunteer work is guaranteed to give you more than the organization gets from you. Giving monetary donations is making an investment in your own spirituality. It is sad but true — your heart goes where you put your money.
7. Read only non-fiction. Stop going to movies. Give up the video games. Empty all that unreal stuff out of your brain and begin to fill it with what is real: life, people, work, play, gardens, pets, ocean, sky, etc.

It is what you do every day that counts. This is true for your physical health as well as for your spiritual well-being. For a spiritual life, you must do spiritual practice. Do the time-honored practices daily. Give up the things that pull you away from your new lifestyle, a little at a time. Most importantly, find a Master. Let your mind and heart be filled by a Master, and you will be led to the One Reality within.

The Body's Wisdom
Vision Magazine, April 2000

The mind-body connection does not exist. Both the mind and body are outward expressions of a common source — the reality of your own existence that lies deeper than both the mind and the body. For there to be a "connection," there would have to be two different things. But the mind and body are not significantly different from one another. This similarity is why you can listen to your body's wisdom to get messages that your mind did not perceive. This is also why you must be suspicious of the messages you get from your body, just as you must be suspicious of the value of the stuff in your mind.

Yoga says that your mind pervades your body. Your mind is a tangible manifestation of your own individuality, an energy field that pervades your whole body. When you think, the thinking happens in various places in your body — not just in your brain. Your brain is a major center of your mind, but your mind extends through your whole body. Modern researchers now agree, which makes it easier for modern yogis to describe these ancient teachings. But it was always true, even when scientists didn't describe it this way.

The problem arises because you identify with your thoughts. You have been trained to emphasize certain kinds of thoughts: the "good" thoughts, the analytical thoughts of how things should be, thoughts about what you want, what you do not want, etc. These thoughts occur in different areas of the brain. Emotions are the mental activities that occur in the other areas of your body. When you think with your body, you do not call it thoughts. You call it emotions or feelings. If you do not like these feelings (the mind's activity in the body), you shut them down by shutting down your body. Therefore, turning to your body to find its "wisdom" is actually a way of discovering a part of your mind that you were ignoring!

However, there is a trap in looking for your body's wisdom. When you focus too much on the body, you end up identifying with it. You already have a tendency to do this. It shows up even in yoga classes, "How do I look in this yoga pose?" Yoga does make an improvement in how your body looks and feels, but that is not its purpose. Yoga attunes you to inner wisdom — which is significantly more profound than the wisdom that comes from your body.

Your body does not actually have any wisdom. It has instincts, like animals. If we all lived at the animal level, there would be many more violent crimes than there are now. If you follow your body, you end up like the animals: eating, drinking, sleeping, procreating and excreting all your life long. As a human being, you have the potential for much more.

You must recognize the reality of both your body and mind, and then look beyond that superficial level to find the source from which they both arise. There is a deeper and more significant level of reality to your being. When you find this inside, you will still need your body and mind. They become avenues through which that deeper reality is expressed into the world and into your life. Look within. Cultivate this deeper knowing of your own being. You are not your body. You are not your mind. You are not your body and your mind put together. You are so much more!

The Face of God
Vision Magazine, September 1998

It was my first trip to India. It had come together in just three short weeks from idea to airplane. As an economically challenged single mother of three children, it was far beyond my expectations that "dabbling" in yoga and meditation would take me all the way to India. Once there, it somehow seemed so natural to wake every morning at 3 a.m., and to spend the day chanting, meditating, and working in the *ashram* (residential yoga center).

After ten days of the *ashram* routine under the direction of the resident *Guru*, I settled in one day for the afternoon nap. At the end of the hour, I could not wake myself up. I dimly heard the other women in my dormitory room as they quietly dressed. They left to resume their day of spiritual practices. I sunk deeper until I submerged into a delicious unconsciousness, an inner space that has no time.

Abruptly, I awoke terrified. Still lingering before my inner gaze was the echo of a face, fading away faster than I could hold onto. I had seen the face of God! I wanted to go back inside and see it again. The fear that awoke me became an incredible longing to see that face again, or at least to stay in the awe without bolting awake. I dove inside ... or rather, I tried to. I could touch the edges of that sleep, which I now know was deep meditation, but I couldn't find my way inside.

Reluctantly, I arose and dressed. I meandered through the gardens heading vaguely toward the main courtyard, still remembering the face of God. Actually, I couldn't remember the face, only that I had seen it. I was consumed in the memory, and in the desire to see it again.

My *Guru* was sitting quietly in the courtyard. I had seen others go up with questions in these informal times, though I had not yet done so. I knew I must ask how I could see God again, for no one else could possibly know. I approached, knelt and said, "I saw the face of God." He listened to me and looked at me silently. I realized I had not asked a question, so I blurted out, "I want to see it again." "Aaaah," he smiled, "You will." I wondered when that would be, but did not think to ask. I took a seat and stayed in that sweet silence as we sat there together. Then he arose and went inside.

I never forgot that I saw the face of God, but I did forget to look for it. Maybe I never really knew how, for it had been a gift of grace. Grace gave me many years of study and sitting silently with my *Guru*. Then his span of years on earth ended. I continued my yoga and meditation practices diligently for a time, and then I lost even those. Finally that inner yearning became too painful to ignore. Ten years after that first journey, I traveled to India again. I went to celebrate my *Guru's* life on the third anniversary of his death.

Planes arrive in India late at night. I stayed in a hotel to await the morning light and the taxi that would take me to the rural *ashram* the next morning. I awoke before the sunrise, gripped with agonizing grief. Though I knew and felt his presence inside me, only at that moment did I realize my *Guru* was gone. I could not contain it in silence. My travel companion awakened as I began to cry. She sat with me. She held me. Nothing helped. Finally, she pulled out her chanting book and began singing the morning chant, a Sanskrit text honoring the *Guru*.

I paced the floor, but began to feel calmer as his undeniable presence became more tangible. I was standing on the balcony looking at the lightening sky as she reached a verse I knew well. The Sanskrit poetry describes that the *Guru* is beyond form, beyond words and beyond time. As I looked into the sky, I recognized again the face of God. That face was the sky, the whole sky. God was always looking at me, and I hadn't known.

Now I know I am always bathed in His sight, supported by His presence and His love. I look up at the sky frequently. I always see the face of God. This has continued to develop and deepen in the intervening years. Now, I see the face of God in every face, and in the light that shines through everyone's eyes. I know God is looking through my eyes, too.

Relationship
Vision Magazine, October 1998

I was shocked when the *swami* (yoga monk) teaching a philosophy course said, "Relationship is yoga." I had come to India to study, and still harbored a secret desire to be in a cave somewhere high in the Himalayas. Instead, I was in an *ashram* with nearly 1,000 other seekers, all of whom were clearly *not* enlightened beings. At least it was clear to me! Now this teacher was telling me that I was not a yogi unless I was good at relationship. I simply could not take it in, so I completely forgot that teaching for over ten years. Now I can say that yoga has given me not only the ability to be in relationship but to fully enjoy relationship. This is because yoga has given me a sense of Self.

If you did not have a perfect childhood, you might have not completed the process of defining yourself as a distinct and unique individual. Many of your personal traits might unknowingly be an expression of "unfinished business." You cannot blame the others in your life for this, because your *karma* gave you the perfect family for you. Thus, if you were not raised by enlightened beings, yoga says that you must accept that this is the consequence of your actions in previous lifetimes. *Get to work on cleaning up your karma.* You might even uncover a deep gratitude to all those pivotal people in your life for making your *karma* so obvious to you.

Now you can complete that personal work of defining your sense of self. Your sense of self is the key to relationship. Yoga describes different levels of self: the constructed self (*ahamkara*) and the true Self (*atman*). When you ground yourself in true Self, you engage in your activities and relationships from an inner sense of joy and inner fullness. Losing track of that deep essence, you resort to constructing your sense of self through your activities and your relationships. When your activities are successful, you can feel that you are a good person. When your relationships go well, you feel that you are lovable. And when things do not go well, you feel worthless. This places an incredible pressure on the people in your life. The people around you have to say the right things at the right time in order for you to feel good. If they blow it, you feel that you are worthless, and then you take it out on them!

Yoga opens your inner dimension, which provides your inherent sense of worthiness and lovability. If your partner forgets to say, "I love you," you do not feel abandoned and needy. You do not depend on other people in the old (too familiar) ways. When they are caught up in their own stuff, you understand and support them better than ever before. Your whole sense of self is supported from your own inner Source.

When you can see the possibility of living this way, you may begin to question why you need these people in your life at all. It is true; you do reach the point where you do not need them. Still, you can *choose* to still be in relationship with them. In fact, your relationships may significantly improve when they are not based on need any more. Instead they are based on love and joy. The choice to be in relationship is an expression of your inner experience of deep fullness. It even becomes a way of increasing it.

You have experienced this when you have returned home after a yoga class, feeling so full inside, and then you got to share it with someone you love. What if you could live your life this way, all the time? That is relationship! Do more yoga.

Passion and Dispassion
Vision Magazine, July 2001

I was horrified when I first heard that yoga teaches the practice of dispassion. I had been studying intensively for about two years, living in *ashrams* (residential yoga centers) in India and the USA. I was studying yoga poses along with diving deeply into meditation and the principles of yoga philosophy. Though I had read about *vairagya* (vay-rah-geeah), dispassion or detachment, one day I suddenly realized that this teaching threatened my whole way of life. I had always prided myself on being a passionate person. It was my passion that had fueled my jets, took me all the way to India and deep into yoga's mysteries. Now, yoga was telling me to practice dispassion. This was frightening, and confusing.

I looked up "passion" in the dictionary. The first definition listed is suffering. I was shocked! Passion had been associated in my mind with pleasure, with motivation, with commitment and with zeal. I was not only passionate about sex, but about everything in life. I had spent years intentionally cultivating a passion for life itself. Now Webster was telling me that passion is suffering. As I read on, the dictionary explained that this was related to the "passion of Christ on the cross." Okay — but what has that got to do with me and with how I have been looking at my life? It took several days of contemplation to illumine the connection — all my so-called passion for life arose out of my suffering. I had been thrusting myself into one experience after another in order to lift myself up out of the pain and despair that had defined my life since childhood. I *liked* living on the edge. It made me feel alive, which was a big improvement. Passion, for me, was an antidote for suffering.

I then realized there was another level to look at. Everything I was passionate about caused me pain. This included my personal relationships as well as my work, my hobbies and my university studies in psychology. Yoga gave me another tool to dig more deeply into the reservoir of pain that I carried with me everywhere I went. Hey, I could even use the yoga poses to cause pain! This realization uncovered the deepest addiction I had yet found in myself — an addiction to pain. I used pain to define myself and to gauge my progress on the path of self-discovery. If I was not in pain, I felt I was not growing. I truly used pain to feel alive.

By this point, I had only scratched the surface on yoga's teachings on dispassion. Those initial discoveries were really about passion and about addiction, instead of about dispassion. It was then clear to me that this was not an overnight cure for a lifetime of misery. I have now spent over twenty-five years studying and contemplating yoga's teachings. I can testify that the practice of dispassion sets you free from addictions and from pain. Dispassion creates an independent and self-sourced experience of continuing joy that makes life worth living.

However, I think that "dispassion" is a dangerous word. I rarely use it when I am teaching — I translate *vairagya* in other terms, because it is so easily misunderstood. Dispassion is not the same as disconnection. It is not meant to create a withdrawal from others or from life. Our society is inherently disconnected. We take this word "dispassion," and use it to isolate ourselves, to become insular and lonely. Yoga develops an incredible inner attunement, not an insular, unfeeling, meaningless charade. Yoga's inner attunement makes you vibrate with the bliss of consciousness, found at the foundation of your own existence. Then, you do not depend on anything outside of you to create your experience of joy. This means that you are no longer dependent on talking with a certain person or on having that pint of ice cream at midnight. You do not have a bad day just because your friend or a co-worker was in a funk. You are not waiting for a beautiful sunny day before you can find the light inside. You live in that self-sustaining light all the time, and you carry it with you everywhere you go.

Remember the little kid in the comics that walks around with a cloud over his head — was it not Pigpen? What if you changed the cloud into a radiant sun shining over your own head? Let it illumine your work, your relationships, your whole life. Instead of being passionate about life, live with enthusiasm, with delight, with commitment, with zeal! Instead of passion being your jet fuel, dispassion gives you a life of enthusiasm without pain. The delight on the inside becomes accessible through the practice of dispassion.

A Yogi in the Real World
Master Yoga Academy, September 2001

This was written a few days after the terrorist attacks of September 11, 2001. I have retained the language, even though it was so time-sensitive. It addresses the issues of that moment, while looking at the larger questions that every yogi must face.

What Should I Do?

It is terrible. It is horrible. It is real — the World Trade Center towers are gone, as are so many human beings. I practice *ahimsa*, non-harming, but clearly there are others in the world who do not. How can I move through this world as a yogi? What can I think and say, what should I do, how do I deal with my feelings? This is the question that Arjuna asked Krishna in the *Bhagavadgita*. Coincidentally, I was teaching from the *Bhagavadgita* when we got the news on Tuesday morning. We went from the text to life itself, and found that they are the same. *Abhyasa* (continued practice, diligent and consistent) and vairagya (letting go, again and again) will keep you sane in this crazy world, peeling the layers of the *kleshas*, the root contractions that cause all your suffering:

1. When you feel *abhinivesha* (fear, terror or anxiety), look into it. You find aversion – afraid you might have to experience something you don't want to experience.
2. *Dvesha* (aversion, shock or horror) are covering an unrecognized desire – you want it to be a different way. It isn't, but you want it to be.
3. Peel away *raga* (the feeling of desire) instead of indulging it, you find your own limited and dependent sense of self – how you construct your sense of "who-you-are" and "how-you-are" by watching the landscape (tracking what others around you are doing and by how they are feeling).
4. Peer closely into that limited sense of self *(asmitaa)*, you find a feeling of not being enough, an inadequacy that you can never make up for, no matter what you do or say – because you do not know the true reality at the deeper level of your own being.
5. Look inward, past that foundational not-knowing *(avidyaa)*, and you find that you are consciousness, the fully expanded divine Reality that exists in complete ecstasy. You see that everything that exists is a manifestation of that One, including you and everyone and everything around you, even including the events of the last few days.

The trick is that we have to do the stair steps. We have to do them again and again. In a time like this, we have to do them more. Do more yoga. Do the asanas, or breathe. Repeat a mantra — offer each repetition to someone in pain. Chant when you drive. Peel the layers again and again, using every tool you know. This is the real yoga.

How About the Way I Feel?

I have watched my own range of responses to the events of the last few days. I have found that every thought and feeling fits into one of three categories.

The World

The world has changed. We used to be able to count on airplanes arriving at their destinations and people going to work and returning at the end of the day. It has all been turned upside down. More accurately, that old world is blown to bits. We navigate our life by landmarks: the house with the big tree out front where I turn left to go home, the people I see every day, or the shape of the New York City skyline. Some of those landmarks are gone. New ones have appeared. The outer landscape has changed.

I find myself holding my breath sometimes, waiting for it all to pass and everything to "go back to normal." But it will not. When things do settle, it will be a new "normal." The needs of my students have changed. The things I used to say to help students with their minds might work now, or they might not. What they need has changed because their thoughts have changed, because the world has changed.

Feelings of shock and anger are widespread reactions. Fear that something could happen turns into constant anxiety. Irrational fear has you closing the drapes and locking your bedroom door at night, even as you know that it cannot stop an airplane from flying into your building.

Denial and avoidance sound like this. "It is so surreal." "I keep thinking it is a dream and I'll wake up. Then everything will be fine." It looks so much like a scene from a movie that you have to keep watching the plane fly into the building, so you can try to fathom that it is real. At one point, they announced that they had removed 5,000 tons of rubble (10 million pounds) and it has not made a dent in the pile that is over seven stories tall. They call it "Ground Zero," like the point where the bomb exploded in Hiroshima.

The continuing changes in our world will include new security measures at airports and other public buildings. There will be the political and military effects. These will have a real effect on your life, which may take years to play out. Yes, the world has changed. You must know this. As a yogi, you must know and accept the world you live in. You can also choose to work to change it, but you must begin by knowing and by accepting the reality of what does exist. This is the new "it."

At the same time, you can (and you must) honor the lives of those who have died. Pray for and offer your help to those who survive. And remember, one of the survivors is you. So, send your prayers and blessings to all who are in pain, including yourself.

My Understanding of the World

In California, there is no smoke in the sky. Relatively few of us have family or friends who were in those buildings or airplanes. There are no external signs of change. Everything goes on the same, but it isn't the same at all. The biggest change is in the inner landscape.

Your chances of a violent death have not really increased at all. There is still the ever-present danger of a car accident. Your chances of getting cancer or being killed in an earthquake, hurricane, flood or other natural disaster haven't changed. I know of a nineteen-year-old college athlete who just dropped dead in the middle of a workout, for no reason that the doctors can find. You have always been at risk, in every moment. Death stares you in the face.

What has changed is your sense of self. This sense of "me" is based on the outer landscape. External changes impose an unexpected (and unwanted) change in the "me." As an American, that sense of self-included complacency about the reality of the world. The "favored status" that Americans have enjoyed is gone. We now know the threat of terrorism is real, is personal and is daily.

The illusory sense of self was the real target, not the buildings or the people in them. Let it go. You must let go of the illusory sense of self every time you become aware of it. If these events can make you aware of where you get stuck in your superficial sense of self, use them to propel yourself forward on the path of transformation and transcendence.

If you think the world has changed, you are suffering from major myopia (nearsightedness). You are now seeing reality. This is only the most recent event in decades of attacks on innocent civilians. People throughout the world live under the constant threat of terrorism. Continuous wars have raged simultaneously in multiple locations for the last several decades. Unfortunately, the planet is never without war and terrorism. America was safe, we thought.

The chain of violence has been escalating in the U.S., from the gunman killing the McDonald's customers in San Diego, the ex-employee shooting up the post office, the Oklahoma City bombing, and now the teenagers shooting each other in high school. Teens have always been the "canary," playing out society's undercurrents in stark living color. The movies and spy novels, along with the video and Internet games, laid the whole scenario out in detail long before it became reality. Unfortunately, it is now closer to home than any of us wanted. And that makes you look at the world and at yourself in a different way than before. Your inner landscape has changed. Who are you now?

Deeper Inside

It is so easy to take on the heaviness. Having been developing the subtle levels of awareness, it is too easy to feel everyone else's pain and to take that on, or to lose myself in it. I can cry and wear a long face, lost in grief, to prove to the world (and to myself) that I care. I can obsess on the minutiae of the constant press reports, talking with everyone about the latest developments. I can indulge myself in agitation, anxiety and fear. I can develop a righteous anger and cry out for retribution.

To go in a different direction, I can take on the persona of being spiritual. I can hold myself together through constant effort, and become exhausted from the strain of appearing to have it together. I can project an aura of peace and serenity that will calm those around me, while I suppress my own undercurrent of turmoil. Or I can continue on with the daily tasks, completing the incoming emails and preparing for the upcoming courses, pretending that nothing has happened. I can ignore it all.

All of these are true possibilities, but are still choices of how to be stuck at the superficial level of being. If you make your choices at this level, you are not really a yogi. You must dig deeper. You must find that deeper dimension of your own being, for it is always there. It is from this level that the inner support

235

arises and the healing comes. It is from this foundation of being that peace spreads through me and all around me.

I cannot support or serve others effectively when I am coming from despair or dismay. Yet, I cannot withdraw and deny the reality of life's events in order to create or protect my "state." That state must become completely portable. It must be poured into each conversation, each email, and every continuing breath. I must dive deeper in order to be of genuine service, not merely to fulfill my selfish desire to be calm and happy.

If yoga were about diving deeper by leaving the world, it would be too easy. Worse, you would be on a path of awareness that depended on you cutting off awareness. Your primary practice of becoming less aware of the world would be your means of cultivating awareness. You would be trying to overcome ignorance (being not-enlightened) by cultivating stupidity (not-knowing of the tangible and material realm). This could never work. You are called to a higher goal.

You must practice ahimsa, even if the rest of the world does not. Patanjali listed it as a key practice several thousand years ago, which means that the world was not a peaceful, non-harming place then. It is not now, either. At the same time, you must be the warrior. You are Arjuna, on the battlefield with Krishna's advice ringing in your ears. You must be active in the world, for new reasons. You must cultivate the ability to stay open to everything that happens. Accept it as it is, and be who you are. Only then can you help. Only then can you serve. This is the only way you can fulfill your life's purpose. You must live up to the highest purpose of life, even if others do not. Do not allow others to make you close up. When you close up on the outside, you shrivel up on the inside. You must stay completely open, outside and inside. If that means you cry, then cry. If that moves you through stages of fear and anger, then go through it — but do not "be" it. You are consciousness. So is everyone who died. So is everyone who mourns someone who died. So is everyone who was involved in creating this horrendous event. It is all consciousness.

I offer blessings and prayers for all.

Addictions

Vision Magazine, February 1997

Addictions are a desperate attempt to live in bliss. You have a baseline require-
ment for bliss, which you can call your Bliss Quotient (BQ). When you are not
meeting your BQ, you go looking for something to create bliss. Unfortunately,
the places you look have side effects. If the side effects damage your health,
your mind, or your life, it is called "addiction." Drugs and alcohol are fairly easy
to clarify this way. Now it is clear that food can fit into the addiction category.
Work and exercise can also be addictions. All of them are used as catalysts to
the inner experience of bliss. You may be using them to meet your basic BQ.
Ram Dass once described how he decided to live in bliss by staying high on
LSD all the time. He discovered after several days that it was impossible,
because he could not handle basic life needs (like eating), and because the
side effects were damaging his body. So he decided to go to the bliss experts,
the yogis in India.

The ancient sages explain that you desire bliss because it is your nature. But,
you are currently cut off from your true nature. Yoga, "union," is the resolving of
this inner split so that you experience the natural bliss of your own Being. The
internal split shows up in your internal dialogues — the endless conversations
you have with yourself inside your head. It shows in your stooped posture and
habitual facial expression, in your relationships (which often have a disturb-
ingly repetitive quality), in your Freudian slips and more. It is easier to see
others' internal splits than to see your own. Yet the split is there or you would
be living in constant bliss, and you wouldn't need anything external to trigger
it.

Bliss that is triggered by externals is temporary bliss. If your bliss comes from
roller blading, you will only be in bliss while you are roller blading, or while
you're talking about roller blading, or planning to go roller blading or buying
roller blading supplies and magazines, etc. Your focus on roller blading will be
complete, because roller blading is your catalyst to bliss. All your friends will
take up roller blading, or you will make new friends with people you meet on
wheels. When does it become defined as an addiction? Perhaps you could get
a job teaching roller blading, in marketing or designing improvements in the
products. Is it an addiction yet?

Yoga says the problem is not about addiction. The problem is that your bliss is temporary. It only happens when you are roller blading. You have a low BQ. Where is your bliss when you are eating or sleeping? What about your work and relationships, or when you are stuck in a traffic jam? You are stuck with "dependent bliss," meaning your bliss depends on something outside of you and is only temporary. Also, your bliss from roller blading is only partial. You are not a "perfect" roller-blader. You may fall down, or you have imperfect form. Or perhaps you are really good at it but your mind keeps running the litany of all your problems even when you are rolling along.

Bliss is more accessible than you think, but you have been looking for it in the wrong place. You need "independent bliss," not "dependent bliss." What you really want is the joy of being alive, like when you were a six-month-old baby and woke up with the sunrise every morning. Your parents might not have been joyful at that time in the morning, but you were *alive* and *awake* and *ready for life*. How can you get back to that?

Yoga is the Science of Bliss. Every technique of yoga is for the purpose of increasing your bliss. The first stage of bliss is relaxation, which progresses to a tingling aliveness throughout your whole body. Then it becomes a contagious joy that arises from inside, without any external cause. This bliss is more than merely physical. It can be accessed by a variety of yoga practices including yoga poses, breathing, chanting, meditation, contemplation, study of the ancient texts, and serving others.

Addictions are obsessions. Your mind obsesses on a means of getting bliss. That mental fixation impels you to repeat the activity that worked in the past. Even yoga can become an addiction, but there is a big difference. The bliss that yoga gives you is reliable and long-lasting. It has no negative side effects. It is cumulative, which means that the same yoga practices increasingly give you more bliss. Best of all, yoga frees you from all addictions because it gives you direct access to the bliss of your own Being. "Life without bliss is a wasteland," Joseph Campbell said.

It is the nature of your mind to obsess on things. Your mind is trying to help you raise your BQ by obsessing on the things that have catalyzed bliss for you in the past. In addition, your mind is trying to help you raise your BQ by planning things so that you will experience bliss in the future. But your mind is missing the moment, for the *now* is where the bliss is. When you bring your mind into the present with your body (where you are located right now, what you are doing right now), you will experience bliss. At least you will relax, which is the first stage of bliss.

Each of the practices of yoga is for the purpose of stilling the relentless activity of your mind. That mental activity and the underlying anxieties distract you from the inherent bliss within you. Yoga quiets your mind so you can discover the bliss that is inside you. It has always been there. Bliss is what you experience when you are not worrying, ruminating or analyzing your life. It arises naturally when you quit looking for something outside of you. Yoga teaches you how.

Addictions are our "norm." Unfortunately, this "norm" or "being normal" is not a state of health or happiness. You have to actively do something to get out of the rut that everyone else is in. But you cannot do it with the tools you already have at hand. All the tools you have already learned to use, continue to produce what you have already experienced. Do you describe yourself as truly healthy and completely happy? The Western emphasis on rational-logical mind is excellent for business and competition, but not very useful for bliss. The question is, "Can an old dog (you) learn new tricks?" Try yoga!

Your Health Is Your Karma
Vision Magazine, October 1996

Your health is your *karma*. The structure of your genetics is the physical manifestation of your past *karma*. Your DNA is a map of the physical *karma* that brought you back into life. Yoga says that it is changeable. Gene research indicates that genes are not completely fixed; some of them jump around and can mutate. Scientists freely admit they do not understand it all. The difference is that yogis do not try to understand it—they use yoga's proven tools to change it. You can change your health by changing your *karma*.

The most important thing to understand about your *karma* is that there's no one else you can blame. You did it to yourself. *Karma* is the rebound of the tennis ball that you threw against the wall last week, last year or last lifetime. Whatever you do has its strongest effect on you. If you treat other people respectfully and live a good life, the one who benefits most is you. If you try to cut corners, lie or take advantage of others, you will be living with a cheat and a thief — yourself. The world helps you get the lesson by reflecting back to you what you do not see about yourself. In other words, "it is in your face." It is in your body, too.

Some people say you can heal an illness by changing your thinking. This is true sometimes. Sometimes it is not true. When it is not true, you can end up worse off because now you feel guilty about being unwell. When you can change your health by changing your thinking, you must include the subconscious and unconscious levels as well. A woman once shared her morning routine with me, "I get up every day, look in the mirror and give myself a big smile, saying, 'You are wonderful! You are beautiful! You are fantastic! Today is a great day!'" As she described this, she put on a big fake smile and got very perky and animated. But her eyes never changed ... neither did her body, which was racked with pain ... nor did her life change. She had many challenges, both financial and family stuff. Her conscious message to herself had not reached the subconscious and unconscious levels.

The most important thing to understand about *karma* is that, while you created it, you can also change it. If what you are experiencing now is the result of past actions, then what you experience in the future will be the results of current actions (still mixed with some old unfinished business). Yoga offers powerful tools for changing your *karma*. Some of the tools are familiar and some are new. If you want to change your *karma*, here's a list of how to begin:

CHANGE YOUR BODY: Whether it is your health you want to improve or the way you look, here are some are basics:

> Exercise: Any kind of exercise is beneficial. Yoga poses can be done as exercise, but they are actually much more. In *Svaroopa Yoga*, the poses reach deeper than your body and begin changing your *karma*. Old patterns get cleared away, clearing the subconscious and unconscious levels of mind at the same time. Last week, a student described it in a yoga class this way, "It feels like I took a toothbrush into my bones and scrubbed out everything that did not belong there."

> Food: Improve your diet by whatever plan most interests you (vegetarian, raw foods, low fat, macrobiotic, etc.). Choose what eating plan suits you. There is not one right answer for everyone, which is why there are so many to choose from. Yoga recommends a vegetarian diet but allows dairy products in moderation. The classical yoga diet is also the Ayurvedic diet, which means it is personalized for your basic constitution and current needs.

> Relaxation: The activities you plan for your relaxation time are not the true quietude that yoga prescribes. True relaxation is the cessation of all activity (outer and inner), which means you would turn off the television, radio, CD player, etc., and rest in quietude for a few minutes every day. This is not sleep either, but a more restful stillness that you give yourself daily (ten- to twenty-minutes). Most yoga classes include this at the end of every class. There are many relaxation tapes available (Hint: Look for "relaxation" tapes, not "guided visualization" tapes that actually activate the mind). This conscious choosing of physical stillness has a profound effect on your body as well as your mind, which starts us on the next category.

CHANGE YOUR MIND: I used to be cautious about suggesting to students that they needed help with their mind. I recently realized that everyone knows they need help with their mind!

> Gratitude: Even if your life is not perfect, there are many blessings for which you can express gratitude. Begin by counting your blessings. Then go one step further and express gratitude for them. Say thank

you to the people who bring blessings in your life. Try saying thank you to your employer for your job. On your birthday (or any day), say thank you to your parents for bringing you into the world and raising you in the best way they knew how. Say thank you to the ocean and the sky, to the flowers and birds and sunshine. Express your thanks for the freeways, even if there are other cars on them, too. Have a conversation with God, or nature, or with whatever you consider to be the source of all of this. Look for things to be grateful for and express your gratitude frequently.

Meditation: Do it. Even if you think you do not know how. Just sit down, set a timer, and stay there until the timer goes off. Even if your mind keeps going the whole time, stay there. Even if your body aches, stay there. Every time your body or your mind distracts you from your meditation, tell it lovingly, "I will deal with that in just a few minutes." Later, keep your promise and deal with the physical or mental issues that need your attention. Your mind will begin to trust you. It will become your friend. Then it will become quiet when you choose to sit quietly. You will find who you really are — the true Self that is different than your mind.

Live in the present: Researchers now say that you think 65,000 thoughts a day. Most of them are about the past or the future. If even 10 percent of your thoughts were new, you'd have a very interesting mind. But it is mostly playing reruns. If you mind were replaying the most beautiful and significant moments of your life, it would be interesting. Unfortunately, it obsesses on the worst stuff! So, stay in the present moment. Even if the present moment is not great, it is better than what your mind wants to do. This means that when you're filling a glass of water; keep your mind with you, mentally filling the glass of water. Do not waste your mind remembering how your favorite glass got broken, or thinking about the new kitchen faucet you wish you could buy. Keep your mind in the present, filling the glass of water. Treat your mind as if it is a helium balloon: put a string on it and tie it to your wrist.

CHANGE YOUR LIFE:

Service: Yoga calls this "*karma yoga.*" You become free from *karma* through the yoga practice of serving others. Volunteer with an organization or cause that you believe in. Show up to help, even if what you're doing is simple stuff. Every organization needs some help with taking out the trash, putting labels on envelopes, running errands, greeting people at events, etc. If you keep showing up, they start to give you things that are more interesting or challenging to do. Now is when you really have to be careful, because it is not *"karma yoga"* if you are doing it for the wrong reasons. If you want to get ahead in the organization, if you are hoping for the T-shirt or trophy they give out at the end of the year, or if you want to take a course they give in return for a certain number of hours of your work — oops! It is only true service when it is giving while expecting or desiring nothing in return. This is one of the most powerful ways to clean up your *karma*.

Dharma: *Dharma* means living your life responsibly. Take care of the things for which you are responsible. This includes taking care of yourself as well as the things you are supposed to do. Do all the things you know you are supposed to be doing, *willingly*. The *Bhagavadgita* defines yoga as "skill in action." Do the best you can at each thing you do. Find that part of yourself that hangs back and bring it along with you for a change. Be a responsible, actively involved, willing participant in life, whether you are at work, home or at play.

Non-harmfulness: "Above all, do no harm." This oath of the ancient physician is also a primary principle of yoga, *ahimsa*. As you do all the things required by *dharma*, do not cause harm to anyone or anything. Living in this way, you walk lightly upon the earth. You treat others with compassion and respect. It means: "Do not cause harm to others," but it also means, "Do not hurt yourself!" This takes us back up to the top of the list, where you begin with the basics of taking care of your body and mind.

Changing your *karma* is easy, because you create your own *karma*. Thus, when you change what you do, your *karma* changes, too. Changing your *karma* is the only way to get out of the repetitive cycle you are caught in and to find freedom. Changing your *karma* takes some effort, like turning a steering wheel in an old pickup truck. Once you have started the truck going in that new direction, it is easy to continue. You can begin by picking one item from the list above. Do it for three days in a row. You will feel so good that you'll never want to go back to the old way.

Reincarnation
Vision Magazine, August 2001

The ultimate purpose of life is much greater than you can hope to accomplish
in one lifetime. It would be far too limited to have only one lifetime worth of
potential. Reincarnation is yoga's description of how it works. It is becoming
quite a popular theory in America. There are television shows with the host
describing the past lives of audience members. Scientific research has recently
validated reincarnation so thoroughly that no one can refute it, unless they just
really *want* to have a closed mind. <u>USA Today</u> recently published statistics
showing that over 60 percent of Americans believe in reincarnation. Ministers
quote Bible passages to support it. You can even go to a past-life regression
therapist — but I recommend you do not! More about that later . . .

Technically called "the doctrine of the transmigration of souls," reincarnation
teaches that life is truly and ultimately fair. If you do something that harms
another person, you will go through that same experience of pain yourself. If
you do something that serves and uplifts another, you will be served and
uplifted. What you put out comes back to you, in this lifetime or the next.
Since it is impossible to balance it all in one lifetime, the balancing out carries
into future lifetimes. If your actions were extremely bad, you cannot bear the
consequences in a frail human body. So, you go to hell — but not for eternity.
In this way, God's universe is compassionate as well as completely fair. Once
you have balanced out the painful actions, you get another chance as a human
being. Similarly, good actions can take you to heaven, but not for eternity. No
one is consigned to hell forever, but no one gets to heaven forever either. The
reason is that the ultimate goal is better than heaven. More about that later,
too . . .

The key to understanding reincarnation is to understand your power of choice.
As a human being, you have free will. You are able to make choices. Many of
your life experiences are *karmic* — the results of actions you chose in prior
lifetimes. This shows up most strongly in your childhood. The family into
which you were born was your *karma* — the result of your past actions. You
chose the prior actions that led to the current life experiences.

When you understand reincarnation, you will very naturally take on full
responsibility for your situation. It does not matter whether you are creating it

now, through your current actions, or if it is due to you from prior lifetimes. Don't just lie around in your misery, blaming someone else! Get going on making new choices. Take action to change your situation, and do it in a positive and uplifting manner. You will create new *karma* that brings joy into your life. Be careful! If your actions come out of anger and revenge, then you create future pain for yourself. Your power of choice and action is called *svatantra*, "free will." How you use it will affect your current life and your future lives as well.

Don't waste your time trying to find about your past lives. Anything from a previous lifetime that affects this life will be "in your face." Looking into your past lifetimes can be another avoidance technique — a way of avoiding looking into the mirror of this life, where you can see yourself fully. Your current life is full of experiences which arise from a mixture of choices made in past lives and choices made in this life. Do not waste your time to figure out which is which. You need every moment available to figure out which choices to make now, and how to best implement them. If you spend time trying to figure out what you did in a past life that gives you this *karma*, you still have the same *karma*. Instead, accept the situation now as though you created it, whether you remember creating it or not. Make a decision about what to do now and about how to do it! This is the best approach to *karma* and reincarnation.

If all you had to do were to make it to heaven, then the goal of life would come after death. Yoga says that life itself has meaning. Life is not about reaching a destination — the meaning is found in the journey. You must perform *karma*-free actions in order to draw closer to the ultimate goal of knowing your Self as Consciousness-Itself. Your choices and actions create what is popularly called "good" or "bad" *karma*. This is based on the quality of your actions, as well as your reason for doing them. These *karmas* trap you in the endless cycle of death and rebirth. Any time you act out of desire for personal fulfillment, you collect more *karma* (good or bad). You are guaranteed to keep coming and going (even to heaven and hell), whether you want to or not.

The way out is by performing your actions as offering. When you offer true service to another human being, or to God, then your action is *karma* free. *Karma* free actions not only free you from future lifetimes. They create your own upliftment in this life. You are ennobled and uplifted when you give from the heart without any desire for repayment or recognition. Be careful — if there is a desire to be ennobled and uplifted, then you still collect *karma* from your action, and remain bound to another cycle of lifetimes. Watch your motivation — that is an important key.

How high does this upliftment go? What is the goal that is even "better than heaven?" Yoga promises that you will live in the completely fulfilling, ever-deepening, inner experience of the one Reality, while living out your full life span. All your choices and actions will be divinely inspired, and spread love and light into the world. At the end of your life, you merge fully into the Source of All Being. This is your destiny, and yoga will take you there.

Pilgrimage
Vision Magazine, November 2001

I walked around the side of the mosque, but found nothing. I walked on around
the next side, and the next. I began to think that my tour guide was sending
me on a wild goose chase, when I finally saw it. There was a woman standing
next to a big metal rack with black tents on hangers. I did not know what to
say, but she spoke no English anyway. She looked me up and down and
reached for the longest one she had. She helped me put on the tent dress and
the head covering. Then she pointed to the side door. I walked into the
women's quarters of the brand new State Mosque of Malaysia.

There were two women already in the little side women's room, facing into the
vast open space. It was huge! I have been to stadiums and theaters in many
cities, but this seemed bigger than anything I had ever seen. There were no
pictures or altars. There was nothing to focus on. A few other women came in
and whispered, then fell silent. I stood, not knowing what to do. More than
that, I didn't even know why I was there.

For twelve years, I had been traveling the globe. I remember my first trip to
India, going there to meet my *Guru*. It seemed impossible for a single mother in
the 1970's, but it had happened! Then I spent years shuttling between what
had become my two homelands. Both were strange in some ways, but familiar
in others. I began visiting other countries on the way, both in the East and
West. I shopped and toured in every country that the airplanes routed
through, sometimes for only a day or two, sometimes for a week or a month. I
filled up the pages in my passport and had to send it in to get more pages
added. Everywhere I went, I visited holy sites. I rubbed gold leaf on Buddha's
belly in Thailand, burned incense in Chinese temples, and visited the great
cathedrals in many countries of Europe. I sat zazen in a temple in Japan,
attended mass in Goa, and offered flowers and coconuts in temples all over
India.

I can see that I had been chasing God all my life. I first found the experience in
nature, beginning when I was a kid at summer camp. The YMCA camp I went
to every year had a lookout point, an incredible view where silence was observed. I spent more time there than in the canoes, arts and crafts and horse-
back riding combined. When I got old enough to choose where I wanted to go,
summer vacations were spent in tents in the Sequoias, taking in the majesty of

trees that were alive at the time of Jesus and Buddha. Niagara Falls overwhelmed me with a surge of joy so great that I couldn't contain it. I ultimately had to surrender — to both the sound and sight of all that water surging over the rim! I spent three days on Mt. Shasta, an incredibly trippy place.

My pilgrimages have taken to me to holy places carved out by nature as well as places built by humankind. The one that stands out most boldly in my memory is the day my knees buckled as I climbed twenty stairsteps to the room in which my *Guru's Guru* had taken *Mahasamadhi* (left his body). Though my visit was sixteen years after the auspicious event, the energy in that room thrust me into a three-hour meditation. It changed something so deep in me that there are still no words for it, even though it is more than twenty years later. This room that he used as the stage for his exit from this world was in a small town that had grown up around him. In America, towns grow up around shopping malls and stadiums. In India, towns grow around enlightened beings.

Now I stood in a mosque. I felt like I did not have a clue what it was about. Slowly, the space in the room took on a different quality for me. Instead of looking at the walls, I began to see the space between the walls. I realized that space was filled with a presence I had been searching for in every holy site I had ever visited. In that moment my search came to an end, as I realized the thread of pilgrimage throughout my life. I found God in a mosque, just as I had in nature and in the churches and temples everywhere.

Shri Ramakrishna practiced all the religions and then said that God is found in every one. I confess that I did not put forth that much effort — I visited rather than practiced them all, but I found that One Reality in every place. Now I don't feel the need to travel any more, because all those pilgrimages have given me something that is not dependent on a location. It is everywhere and also here, all at the same time. But I could not have found it without going to all those places. I highly recommend pilgrimage!

In fact, someone recently showed me a photo of the *murthi* (enlivened statue) of Vitthala in the temple at Pandharpur and chills ran up my spine. Maybe I could actually get to Pandharpur some time soon. Of course, the mouth of the River Ganga is such an auspicious site. There is an *ashram* (residential yoga center) there I have always wanted to visit. *Swami Subramunium* is building a Shiva temple on Kauai and has an incredible crystal *lingam* to install. And, I hear the temple at *Alandi* is incredible. Jnaneshwar Maharaj took live *Mahasamadhi* there over eight hundred years ago, and his presence is still so strong that . . .

Creating a Sacred Space
Vision Magazine, June 1996

You cannot create a sacred space because God already did. You are in it right now. No matter where you are as you read this, it is a sacred space. Probably you were not paying attention to this aspect of your surroundings. There are things you can do to heighten your attentive abilities. There are also things you can do to make the sacredness of a place more tangible. Yoga is a science of consciousness that offers ways to do both. But the place where you are now is already sacred, and so are you.

A sacred place is wherever people notice that quality or feeling that we call "sacred." The key is people. All you really need is to notice that quality or feeling which is everywhere, including inside yourself. You are yourself a sacred space.

A young man decided to go on pilgrimage, though he came from a poor family. He set out on foot, knowing it would take two years or more to walk all the way to Mecca. Having very little money, he relied on the generosity of the people who lived in the villages along the way. The villagers knew that feeding a pilgrim would give them all the benefits of making the trip themselves. He had traveled only three days when he met an old man who was dressed strangely, with many layers of shabby clothing even in summer heat. The eyes of this old man glowed with an inner fire that could only mean that he was either mad or that he had given himself over completely to God.

They shared a tree, waiting out the midday heat in the leafy shade. The young man tried to start a conversation several times, but the old man was not talkative. As the heat abated, the young man explained he would be on his way because his journey was a long one and he could not waste time. "Ha!" cried the old man, "Your trip is the real waste of time!" Horrified at this sacrilege, the young man began to hurry away from this madman. "Go! Go!" shouted the old man, "Hurry through all the days of your life until you die like a dog sucking on a dry bone. Hurry, hurry. And see what you get for all your hurry."

The young man slowed his step and turned to look again, recognizing the truth in the old man's words. He asked, "What should I do instead?" The old man said, "How many coins do you have in your pocket for your trip?" "Three silver and one gold coin." "Give them to me," demanded the old man, "and do your holy walk around me three times, instead of around the stone. You will save yourself all the years of travel and many blisters on your feet."

The young man, without really knowing why, complied with the strange command. He handed over all of his money and walked around the holy man three times. Then his faced changed. A hint of a smile played on his lips as his eyes filled with a brightening glow. He said, "Now I know. I know that which cannot be found on any road, but only within the human heart. I have no need to travel on. But, please, may I stay with you?" The holy man smiled quietly, and gave the boy back his coins, "Go home. Take what you now know, and live your life in full. You will give to others by being what you are. You do not need me any more."

People travel great distances on pilgrimage to many famous places including Mecca, the River Ganga, Jerusalem, Lourdes, the Pyramids, Ayers Rock in Australia, and more. Whatever you find there is just a finding of the sacred inside yourself.

This inner place is what you actually find when you go to a place of pilgrimage, to a quiet place in nature, or to a place of worship. You use the surroundings to trigger your innate capacity to notice something that is always present. You do not have to travel across an ocean to find an environment that will trigger your experience of the sacred. Find it inside. Do more yoga.

I Will Not Fly

adapted from "I will not Fly"
published in *Hot Chocolate for the Mystical Soul*

The pain in my left shoulder blade felt like an ice pick stuck in my bones. It had been a reliable gauge of my stress level for years. I had learned to use it as a reminder that other things existed in life besides the pressures of raising a family and the amount of work necessary to provide a living as a single mother. Then the children were grown and gone. But my work-style persisted: that is, I must do, *do more, do it all!* I took all this with me, including the familiar ice pick in my shoulder blade, to a yoga weekend featuring personalized yoga therapy sessions as well as meditations and yoga classes.

On the third day, my yoga therapist said it was time to "go for it." She held me in a pose that concentrated on my shoulders by pulling my arms back and supporting them there. She held them there far longer than I could have done myself, asking how it felt. It felt great, at first.

After a while longer, the ice pick seemed to be digging deeper. It hurt, but it felt like something important was happening. I decided to stay with it. I breathed long and deep as I broke into a cold sweat. Her voice gradually grew fainter as I submerged into my own inner experience, until it was like a deep meditation. Suddenly I was a bird, sitting on a high tree branch with two other birds. I had folded my wings and was sitting quietly. I could see the ground below, the sky above, and the tops of the shorter trees nearby.

As we sat together, one of the other birds lifted his wings and flew away, looking for food. The thought arose inside me, "I will not fly for food." I knew what those words meant — that hunger and need would no longer motivate me into my old pattern of incessant activity. I continued to sit quietly with the other bird nearby.

Then a flock of birds flew by, and my neighbor joined them. The thought arose inside again, "I will not fly for company." I knew the deeper meaning was that I would no longer be driven by desire for companionship, through sex or simply social interaction. This could no longer drive me into the painful lifestyle I had known so well. So I sat alone. I was content in my aloneness, yet something was incomplete.

Below me, a child ran into the dirt clearing at the base of my tree. He began to call up to me, making human sounds I could not understand. Two older children joined him, and the question arose, "Do I fly?" Inside was a solid and easy, "No, they are no threat. They are only curious."

The children laughed and called together until adults came. The adults began to confer, and I realized they wanted to capture or kill me. They brought equipment, including nets and ropes. Still I would not fly. They threw stones, but I was too high and the stones could not reach me. There was no reason for me to fly, for I was safe.

Finally, someone arrived in a car and carried out rifles, which looked to me like long sticks. Somehow, I knew these sticks could give out smoke at one end, and that they could reach all the way up to me and kill me. Still my inner feeling persisted, until it became words, "I will not fly for fear."

The adults talked, stalked, and finally aimed their guns. A few bullets whizzed by. I knew I could die. But more important to me was the knowing, "I will not fly for fear." Fear would no longer impel me in my life. But would I die?

I sat with that choice, willing to die rather than fly. After seemingly endless seconds ticked by, a voice spoke deep within me. It was a different voice than the thoughts and words I had before. It was a deep voice, God speaking within me, saying, "Fly. Because I made you." At that moment, I leapt into the air. With great joy, I soared to the tune of the impulse inside, "I fly because God made me! I fly because God made me!"

I soared over the trees, toward the horizon. I streaked faster and faster across the top of mountains toward the sea. Powered by joy, I flew higher into the sky, headed home toward God. I knew I would never again feel trapped in the frenetic pace of life, because I could now *choose* to do it all. Now I participate for the only reason worth living, "Because God Made Me!"

And my shoulder pain is gone.

ACKNOWLEDGEMENTS

CR

I always used to read the acknowledgements in various books and wonder, "Doesn't anyone do anything on their own?" Now, I know that the answer is no. It has taken so many people to make this collection possible that I know my list will be incomplete, no matter what I do.

I would like to say thank you to:

My mother, who infused me with the love of God and taught me, by her example, how to serve. My father, who showed me the power of introspection and reminds me in wordless ways of his unconditional love. My children, who brought out both the best and worst in me, and who undertook the task of training me over the last 30 years and more. My teachers in all places and times, especially those who have opened the yoga door for me in so many ways. Baba Muktananda and Gurumayi Chidvilasananda, who are the wind beneath my wings, my reason for doing and being, the means as well as the goal. The texts and sages, who lived and shared the teachings through the ages, that they might be as alive now as ever. All my students, who have taught me how to love and how to teach. *Svaroopa*-style teachers, who inspire me every day with their continuing openings and their service to others. My hosts and the yoga conferences that have supported me and challenged me at the same time.

Though I founded Master Yoga, it has been supported and shaped by so many through the years. I am in gratitude to all who have helped:

Peter Karlen, who gave me the legal structure and the name. Our current Board of Directors and all who have served in navigating this cruise ship through the ocean of consciousness. The teachers, who have touched so many bodies, hearts and minds, and changed so many lives – including mine. The volunteers and staff, who do the work of yoga in such a way that it becomes the yoga of work, even while they are baking in the "karmic microwave."

In addition, some individuals must be named and thanked personally:

Bombay Cathy Stillman – the consummate scientist and yogi. John Hannon, Executive Director and more — who finds clarity amidst the chaos (mostly), and goes above and beyond. James Sweet, my indispensable assistant – who plays the game of point and counterpoint like a master. Deva Prem – who leads with her heart in integrity and dedication to genuine service. Cathy Dante, Casey Gerdes, Tara Mastro – who make sure I communicate clearly and with consistency. Keep asking the questions! Sandy Joubert Amiel, Lauren Eskra, John Ford – who are my hands and arms, extending my heart to all whom you serve. Durga Cynthia Davenport – who supervises the year, while choreographing the dance across the map. Diana Tarankow – for the edits, and more edits, and more edits... Lauren Eskra (again) – for the eye that can design from the heart, and for the heart that just keeps on giving. Sophie Hawkes – for the generous gift of the beautiful cover art. Allison Lever – for a keen eye, loving heart and creative mind. Alicia Isen – for diving in deeper, once again.

And to anyone who I left out, my heartfelt thanks!

254

CREDITS

ᛰ

COVER ART

This monograph by Sophie Hawkes is one in a series depicting her incredibly beautiful visions of inner light seen during Svaroopa Yoga classes and Embodyment^{SM} sessions. In this one, the central light is becoming an opening through which a person begins to appear. The beauty of the art is enriched by the authenticity of the vision, as documented in yoga's most profound teachings. Sophie showed me nearly 100 of these, each one unique, during a training she took with me at Kripalu Center in Lenox, MA. Thank you to Sophie Hawkes of Hudson, New York, for her generous permission to feature this piece on the cover.

CONTEMPLATION QUOTATIONS

Many of the quotations found in the beginning of the articles in Part II have been reprinted from _The Treasury of Spiritual Wisdom_, copyright 1996, with the permission of Blue Dove Press, San Diego, California.

ARTICLES

I Will Not Fly
This article written by Rama Berch was previously published in _Hot Chocolate for the Mystical Soul_, by Arielle Ford, copyright 1998.

_I am not a Sinner, Sacred Body, The Yoga of Earth,
Body's Wisdom, Passion & Dispassion, Your Health is Your Karma,
The Face of God, Hatha Yoga is a Spiritual Path, Reincarnation, Pilgrimage,
Creating a Sacred Space_
These articles have been gently altered since their original appearence in Vision Magazine, published by Unity Press, San Diego, California.

INDEX (A - J)

ᘓ

INDEX (K - Z)

ॐ

✂ RESOURCES LIST ✂

MASTER YOGA EXTENSION
Programs, Courses & Workshops taught by Rama Berch

MASTER YOGA TEACHER INSTITUTE
Svaroopa® Yoga Teacher Training and Advanced Teacher Trainings

Svaroopa® Yoga **CLASSES**
offered by members of the Svaroopa Association of Teachers(SAT)

OTHER PUBLICATIONS BY RAMA BERCH:

CONTEMPLATION JOURNAL:
Seeds of the Soul

VIDEOS:
Svaroopa® Yoga: The Primary Practice
Yoga for Your Back: Svaroopa® Yoga with Rama
Yoga for Pregnancy: Svaroopa® Yoga with Rama

CD'S & CASSETES *(THE CHANTS OF AWAKENING)*:
Ananda: Bliss of Consciousness
Asato: Nectar of Immortality
Ganesha: Beyond Blessings
Krishna: The Song of Divine Lovers
Shivo'ham: Vibration of Consciousness

AUDIO CASSETTES:
Relaxations: Life's Breath - Full Yoga Breath with Rama Berch
Relaxations: Cultivating Awareness - Full Guided Relaxation
Relaxations: Meditation Music - Meditation Music with Rama Berch

For all of the above, contact –
Master Yoga Foundation
450 Pearl Street
La Jolla, California 92037
800-LUV-YOGA
www.masteryoga.org